# RACE AGAINST TIME

## BUILDING A CULTURE OF MINE SAFETY

Gregory M. Anderson &
Stephen R. Rosene

# RACE AGAINST TIME

## BUILDING A CULTURE OF MINE SAFETY

Printed in the United States of America
ISBN: 978-0-9778308-8-6

*Credits*
Design, art direction and production     Back Porch Creative, Plano, TX     info@BackPorchCreative.com

# FOREWORD

Dear Mining Industry Colleague,

It is our privilege to provide society the materials that fuel the economic engines of our nations. Like you, I am extremely proud of this profession. Unfortunately, our industry's reputation has been damaged by a history of too many safety incidents and accidents.

As you know, safety and productivity go hand-in-hand. Safe mines are productive and profitable mines. For those with poor housekeeping and low safety standards, you can bet a paycheck – and will be betting your life – that morale, productivity and profitability are poor as well.

So, how can we make things better?

*Race Against Time* provides an easy-to-read road map about how one individual can make a positive difference. The authors understand the hazards of our environment and offer a blueprint any miner can relate to for building a culture of mine safety.

My experience in many types of mines around the world has convinced me that behaviors are the root cause of almost every safety incident and disaster. We all know there is no silver bullet. Certainly, leadership must provide direction, support and resources, but creating a culture of safety begins with one individual's commitment. The challenge is for each of us who are committed to safety to influence the people around us.

I hope you enjoy this book as much as I have. More importantly, I hope your motivation for working safely is more powerful than your resistance to change and you will commit to making a positive difference by using what you learn to *Build a Culture of Mine Safety.*

Edward C. Dowling
President, CEO & Director
Anatolia Minerals Development Ltd.

# CONTENTS

# INTRODUCTION

Will you be going home from work today? What about the father, mother, son or daughter working next to you?

On average more than 5,900 deaths occur in the mining industry around the world every year. While there are striking operational and safety-related statistical differences among the various mining regions of the world, the fact remains – too many people die.

No one would argue there is risk associated with mining. However, the industry has shown steady improvement in safety over the years and, according to the United States Bureau of Labor Statistics, the U.S. mining industry's occupational injury and illness rate ranks the industry next to the lowest among major industries.

According to the National Mining Association, "…Recognizing that even one serious accident is too many, the mining industry today is better prepared than ever to achieve the ultimate goal of zero fatalities and injuries in the 21st Century ..." which is why we wrote *Race Against Time.*

This book shows you how incidents can be dramatically reduced, even eliminated. *Race Against Time* is also about how each of us impacts safety in the mining industry and how our individual commitment can make a real difference in every miner's life.

Nobody wants a fatality to occur or an injury to happen. Many mining operations try to eliminate these incidents by making safety their number one priority or writing additional safety policies and procedures ... but they fail, time and time again. Why? Because they have left the human element out of the equation.

*Race Against Time* introduces you to a proven process that will help eliminate incidents, not only in mining but also in your everyday life.

It isn't a difficult book to read. Unfortunately, many of its lessons have been tested by those who can no longer tell their stories.

At the end of each chapter, you'll find the "Miner's Lamp," which provides a recap of the key points and sheds more light on the information in that chapter.

We hope you will use *Race Against Time* in your personal journey and will work to continuously improve mine safety wherever life takes you. Remember, real change can only take place where there are open minds and willing hearts.

# THE CHALLENGE BEGINS

"Director of global safety."

Kurt Bradshaw liked the sound of his new position and repeated it as he dialed the phone to give his wife, Jessica, the news.

"Who could have guessed it," he thought. "A fourth-generation miner moving into a Director's office at one of the world's largest mining companies. It's definitely been a long road … but worth the wait."

"I'm so proud of you, Kurt." Jessica's excitement mirrored her husband's. "This calls for a celebration."

"We can also celebrate the raise that comes with the title."

"More money? Even better."

"I'm on the way to meet with my new boss, but I'll see you around 6 p.m."

Sitting in Senior VP of Operations Ron Kaiser's office, Kurt's new responsibilities became instantly more challenging as the man across the desk ticked off his expectations.

"We've got to turn things around," Kaiser was saying. "The new safety policies and procedures we put into place six months ago aren't working.

"We had two fatalities last month at one of our mines in South America," he continued, "along with 10 Lost Time Accidents in South Africa and who knows what we never hear about. Our claims costs … lost productivity … not to mention continual negative press coverage are driving our stock price down.

"Bottom line, Bradshaw, we've tried everything and nothing seems to work, including the zero-tolerance program we initiated last year. So, we need change and we need it fast. We think you're the man for the job.

"You can start with South America or Mexico. Their numbers are high, so pick one of our mines there to be the test site for whatever changes you decide to make … and we want results in 120 days. Then, with any luck at all, we won't keep having the accidents we're having now."

"That deadline doesn't give me much time," Kurt countered.

"That's true, but our reputation in the industry is starting to suffer. We need results." Kaiser's tone let the new director know there was no room for discussion.

Back in his office, and after dealing with a steady stream of well-wishers, Kurt sat and stared at an old photo that had been passed from generation to generation. Kurt had it framed and hung it on his office wall when he first entered management.

It was a shot of the company store at Monongah, West Virginia. A young woman in a simple dress was standing outside, posing on the wooden sidewalk.

That woman was Kurt's great-grandmother, widowed at age 24, when her husband, along with 361 other miners, was killed in 1907 in what would be called "the worst mining disaster in American history." The underground explosion left more than 300 wives without their husbands and 1,000 children without fathers to provide support … which is why Kurt's great-grandmother was working at the company store at the time the photo was taken.

When Kurt had announced he was going to work for the mining company, his father had responded in his usual philosophical way. "This family has given its share of blood, sweat and tears to the mines," he had said in a slow drawl. "I was hoping a college education would lead you so far away from mining, you wouldn't know the difference between a continuous miner and an electric cable shovel."

He had taken the photograph from an old family album, partly to remind himself that his roots were in mining but also to serve as a reminder that each generation of his family had lost members to mining accidents.

He looked at the unsmiling woman in the photograph. She appeared old for her age and her large dark eyes looked as though they'd already seen too much tragedy.

After a few moments, he moved back to his desk and dialed John Sullivan, a co-worker and friend who was on a job in South America.

John and Kurt had become close over the past few years, close enough for their families to spend time together last year when John came to the States for the company's annual meeting.

A native Australian, John had begun his career at the bottom of the ladder and had progressed upward, much the same way Kurt had done … and, like Kurt, John also came from several generations of miners.

"Couldn't have picked a better man, my friend." John sounded genuinely happy to hear Kurt's news. "We'll still be working together. That's the main thing."

"But global safety … it's a huge job … and our numbers aren't impressive," Kurt responded. "Bill Andrews worked hard, putting new policies and procedures in place, but our accident severity and frequency rates continue to rise, which – no doubt – in some small way was the reason they made a change … and Kaiser made it clear, he wants results, so I may be like the proverbial lamb on my way to the slaughter."

"Never let 'em see you sweat, Mate. Besides, I say you're up to the challenge and, if you remember," he chuckled, "I'm rarely wrong."

John's words echoed as Kurt opened the door after dinner at their favorite restaurant that evening. "After you, ladies."

"Don't think I'll eat again until Thursday," Jessica declared.

"Me, too … but I'm going up now … still have homework." His daughter Shannon stood on tiptoe to kiss her dad. "Thanks for dinner … and don't forget, I think you're the best," she whispered before dancing up the stairs.

At 2 a.m., Kurt had yet to close his eyes, thinking of the job ahead of him. "I know operations. I've proven that," he thought to himself, "but safety ... what do I know about safety? It's an entirely different world than operations.

"Besides all the policies and procedures in place, the company has invested millions to upgrade the equipment – with little improvement," he thought to himself as Jessica slept soundly at his side. "What about the program, 'Safety is Our Number One Priority'? Everyone seemed fired up, but then the momentum tapered off, safety disappeared from individual radar screens and the number of fatalities and injuries kept climbing. What's missing ...?"

The next morning at breakfast, Jessica poured their second cups of coffee and brushed Kurt's cheek with a kiss. "You look tired."

"Didn't sleep much. Kept thinking about Kaiser's deadline and trying to remember as much as I could about what has been done in the past. Jess, I'm just not sure I'm the right guy for this job," Kurt admitted. "I don't have a background in safety and I have no idea how to stop all the accidents. What do I really bring to the table?"

"Kurt Bradshaw! Standing on the shoulders of three generations of miners, how could you even think you aren't the absolute best man for the job?"

"It's just that I've had some time to think about what Kaiser expects – and it's a tall order...maybe darn near impossible," Kurt said. "You know the old phrase, 'Over-commit and under-deliver?' I'm just wondering if I've over-committed by saying I would take the job."

Kurt's wife listened in silence.

"Just look at what they're expecting," he continued after emptying his coffee cup.

"But remember how much production, not to mention safety, improved when you became manager? Your team would follow you anywhere. How were you able to do that?" asked Jessica.

"I always worked with good people," Kurt countered.

"Your leadership skills, your ability to talk with anyone and provide feedback, your obvious caring for every employee on your team and willingness to help each one of them make the most of their opportunities," his wife continued. "That's what set you apart. That's why management thought you'd be a good global safety director.

"Besides, you come from rock-solid stock," she said, stopping to pour another cup of coffee for her husband. "Everybody in the company remembers your father and what kind of supervisor he was."

Kurt finished his toast and the last swallows of his coffee as he remembered some of his own past achievements as well as the respected legacies of his father and grandfather.

Now it was Jessica's turn to sip her coffee thoughtfully before she looked up. "It may be you're just being modest," she suggested, "but, if you're feeling unsure about the whole proposition, what about some help? Remember Dad's old friend Sam Rollins?"

Kurt remembered the name. Sam Rollins had been honored at an industry seminar a few years ago. "Yeah, I saw him get a safety award a while back. Really impressive background. He's been around long enough to know this industry inside and out."

"Dad thinks so highly of him. You know, they worked together way back when. Sam might be a good sounding board."

"At least he might give me some ideas about where to start," Kurt's mood brightened at the idea. "I'll call him and see if he has time to meet."

As Kurt kissed his wife goodbye, Jessica tucked a slip of paper into his coat pocket. "While you were dressing, I called Dad and got Sam Rollins' number."

"What would I do without you?" Kurt asked between hugs. "See you tonight."

"Good luck, Mr. Global Safety Director," Jessica called behind him.

✦ ✦ ✦ ✦ ✦

"Sam Rollins," a deep, gravely voice answered Kurt's call.

"Mr. Rollins, my name is Kurt Bradshaw. My father-in-law, Hal Rankin, gave me your number."

Explaining the turn of events leading to his call, Kurt was pleased Sam was available the next day.

"Why don't you come to my house tomorrow evening at 6 p.m.," Sam suggested.

✦ ✦ ✦ ✦ ✦

"Ten minutes ahead of schedule," Kurt thought to himself as he turned off the key. Picking up his backpack, he walked across the wide front porch and pressed the doorbell.

Sam answered the door with a wide smile and a generous handshake. "Welcome, Kurt. I'm glad you took me up on my offer to meet here.

Come in, come in. Make yourself at home and I'll get us something to drink."

The foyer was impressive, decorated with plaques honoring Sam's leadership in the mining union and several shelves of photos. Kurt noticed one photo of Sam standing among what appeared to be a crew at a surface mine. Another showed Sam and two people who could be his wife and son. The last photo appeared to be Sam as a child standing among a group of men covered in coal dust.

In a few minutes, Sam reappeared, carrying two mugs of coffee. Kurt noticed the older man walked with a severe limp.

"Follow me. The front porch is comfortable this time of day."

After the usual pleasantries, Kurt got right to the point of his visit. "Sam, I've been in this business for over 10 years, but this is the first time I've had the deadlines and responsibilities for safety I have now," he began. "To be honest, I'm looking for some help on where to start."

Sam stroked his mustache before he answered, his eyes focusing on an invisible scene in the distance. Then his gaze returned to Kurt. "There's no doubt. You have a big job ahead of you, but it isn't an impossible task.

"In a nutshell, your job is to create a strong safety culture for the miners in your company, which means a lifestyle and belief system for everyone who works there now, and in the future, because a 'culture' is made up of group beliefs and behaviors that are transmitted from one generation to the next," Sam explained.

"One of the biggest challenges you'll have in improving the culture that already exists is dealing with human nature and 'old school' behaviors – but, as a manager, I'm sure you've already had a taste of that."

Kurt agreed, eager to hear more.

"In the mining business – in any business – you'll find there are things people do, day in and day out, that put them or someone else at risk. I call these 'at-risk behaviors' and they are the root cause of most incidents. They are also the foundation for what I call the safety pyramid," Sam explained.

As he talked, Sam drew a pyramid on the notepad he had brought with the coffee.

While looking at the pyramid Sam had drawn, Kurt asked, "Why do you say 'incidents' instead of 'accidents?' Don't most companies use the term 'near miss' instead of 'near hit'?"

"You're very observant," Sam replied. "First, I use the word 'incident' because 'accident' implies something happened outside of someone's control, which is not the case 97 percent of the time.

"When you think about it, what's the difference between a near miss and a near hit? So why do we call it a near miss?" the older man continued. "Typically, we use words like 'accident' and 'near miss' to *lessen* accountability or *minimize* the potential consequence – that's literally like whistling past the graveyard...."

Sam paused before going on. "Getting back to that old school mindset," he began after a moment. "A lot of miners believe they have to prove how tough they are to make it in this industry. They've heard stories from their family or friends about proving themselves and this perpetuates many of these at-risk behaviors.

"Remember old school isn't about age," the veteran said. "Today's work force is made up of as many young dinosaurs as it has old ones because the company's culture usually creates them."

Kurt nodded his understanding. "I've seen it many times," he offered. "It's easy for a new-hire to pick up that attitude. In no time at all, you can't tell the newcomers from the old timers. They all work the same. "Mind if I write a few things down while we're talking?"

"Be my guest," said Sam, pausing as Kurt took a yellow pad out of his backpack.

"Another mindset is what I call 'the bullet-proof' mentality,'" Sam continued.

"Bullet-proof folks, particularly young people who've spent several years at the mine, but don't exclude older workers from this group – think they know it all, particularly their jobs … and they don't think they'll ever be hurt. It's that tendency to think, 'Nothing can hurt me because I'm a young, invincible stud' that gets them injured or killed. As they get older, that idea becomes, 'Nothing's hurt me yet, so why should I worry?'

"Take wearing safety glasses, for instance. What do you 'expect' to happen if you don't wear them," Sam asked.

Kurt thought for a moment. "Well, usually nothing except you might get yelled at … or at least that's my experience."

"Exactly!" Sam said, leaning back in his chair. "But, what if – while you were working – something broke and sharp pieces went everywhere or, worse yet, hit you in the face?"

"I'd make sure to wear my safety glasses from that time on."

"Here's another example," Sam said as he swirled the remainder of his coffee around the bottom of the mug. "Miners are notoriously particular about their hardhats. Years ago, we had one guy whose hardhat was, literally, held together with decals he had collected … and he wouldn't give it up for a new-and-improved model. Somebody finally convinced him he'd be safer wearing the new hardhat, but it took some real conversations to get him to make the change."

"Particular? I know what you mean. We've had to have conversations with guys wanting to wear ball caps under their hardhats," Kurt allowed.

Sam paused again so Kurt could catch up with his note-taking. "The at-risk behaviors we take when we're in an old school or bullet-proof mindset – like not wearing the proper hardhat – set the stage for many potential outcomes," Sam explained, drumming the table with the knuckle of a missing forefinger. "You could be lucky enough to never be hit in the head or you could be unfortunate enough to suffer a serious brain injury or even be killed. The only place we have any control over the outcome is at the beginning, at the bottom of the safety pyramid, when we make the choice whether or not to wear our hardhat.

"Here's another question for you," Sam probed. "Do you believe people in the mining industry can do their jobs with zero incidents?"

"Well … I'd like to hope so … but, by its nature, mining has risks and we've come to expect accidents … I mean incidents … will occur," Kurt responded as he tried to become comfortable with Sam's new terminology.

"The issue of 'what we expect' is very important in establishing a strong safety culture," Sam explained. "Years ago in Los Angeles, a new teacher came into a school and was told she would be teaching a class of the school's brightest sixth graders. The principal told her the sky was the limit for these kids.

"At the end of the school year, achievement tests showed this new teacher's class had improved their scores more than any other class in the school. Most of the students in this class had been so hungry to learn, the new teacher had to give them even more schoolwork than they were supposed to get.

"Now here's the kicker. That new teacher was actually given a class with some of the poorest performers in sixth grade. But, because she expected them to do a great job, they did."

"So, how did she manage to improve their performance?" Kurt wanted to know.

"It was all a matter of what the teacher thought about the students – and her expectations," Sam said. "Remember, the principal told her the sky was the limit for her class. That's how the teacher saw the students, and superior performance was what she expected."

"Her expectations had no limit," Kurt commented as he made more notes. "On the other hand, if the principal had told the teacher she was getting a class of poor performers, she might have had low expectations.

"I know my crew had the highest production rate when they knew what my expectations were. I guess the same is true for safety – *people will work to the level of safety expected of them.*"

"Exactly," Sam smiled. "You're a quick study … we're going to get along fine."

Kurt looked across the table, quizzically.

"Oh, don't think this is going to be our last discussion. In fact, I'd like to meet with you on a regular schedule, to discuss your progress and help you develop the process necessary to establish a strong culture of safety," Sam offered. "Notice, I said 'process' rather than 'program' because a program implies it will have an end, and – as you're probably becoming aware – safety is a never-ending effort."

"I'd be glad to meet regularly," Kurt smiled. "I have the next 120 days to make major changes … and I can see I'm going to need all the help I can get."

"Deal," replied Sam, extending his hand. "Looking forward to it."

Driving back to the office, Kurt felt a relief of sorts. "Sam really seems to know his stuff," he said to himself. "On the other hand, with the time frame I've got to work with, Sam needs to help me come up with a way to change our culture fast," Kurt thought as he parked his car, "and with all the various nationalities, types of mines and levels of experience we have in the company, it needs to be a safety process people will use both at work and at home, 24 hours a day, 7 days a week."

 # MINER'S LAMP

**DEFINITIONS:**

1. **At-risk behaviors:** Those actions we take, day in and day out, that put us or someone else at unnecessary risk.

2. **Incident vs. accident:** An accident implies the result is outside a person's control. In 97 percent of the cases, what happens – the incident – is easily within someone's control.

3. **Near hit vs. near miss:** Maintains focus and accountability on the potential consequence.

4. **Old school mindset:** Creates an environment that gets in the way of speaking our concerns.

5. **Bullet-proof mentality:** Thinking we won't be hurt as a result of our beliefs and behaviors.

**ESSENTIAL CONCEPTS:**

✦ Our expectations are core to building a culture of safety and improving performance.

✦ People will work to the level of safety that's expected.

**Fatality**
**Lost Time Injury**
**Recordable**
**Near Hit**
**At-Risk Behaviors**

✦ The Safety Pyramid illustrates how an at-risk behavior can easily escalate to become a Lost Time Injury or even a Fatality. The only place we have control over the outcome is at the base of the pyramid – where we choose to do or allow an at-risk behavior.

# 2 NEW IDEAS, OLD ISSUES

Kurt looked forward to his Friday afternoon meeting with Sam.

"I don't know what I was expecting," Kurt admitted, easing his wiry frame into the big rocking chair on Sam's porch. "I've attended safety meetings at several mines, which didn't offer much in the way of surprises. But, I also spent some time with the miners, consciously observing what they were doing … and almost immediately saw at-risk behaviors, from personnel not using handrails or proper safety equipment to people leaning back to put their feet on the table while they balanced on two legs of their chair and …."

"I imagine you saw more than you wanted to," Sam finished Kurt's sentence. His expression was serious.

"You're right … much more than I expected, so I need your help in sorting it all out," Kurt nodded. "I started by asking people how safe they felt on the job – and their answers varied greatly.

"One guy – probably in his early 20s – said he knew people got hurt, even killed, at work but didn't think it would happen to him … but – and this was unbelievable to me," Kurt said with amazement, "even if he broke an arm or a leg, the guy told me it would be no big deal."

Sam nodded knowingly. "What that guy has yet to figure out is ***everything a person does – from the moment they're born – carries an element of risk … and a person's survival depends on how well they manage those risks.***"

"Another worker," Kurt continued, "who looked as though he had plenty of experience, said as long as he did the job the way he had always done it and nobody had gotten hurt, he didn't think there was any risk.

"Then a couple of people said they thought about safety on the job because they had to. They cited programs and slogans like 'Safety is Our Number One Priority' and admitted they thought it was a joke, but complied with these programs because they were told to and didn't want to lose their jobs.

Kurt took a deep breath. "Sure enough though, when tonnage levels dropped, production became a priority and the focus on safety disappeared.

"Another guy said he practiced safety measures at home as well as on the job … it was a way of life for him. But, here's something interesting. He said he talked with his wife about how slicing vegetables on a cutting board was safer than cutting them while holding them in her hand. But, when it came to the job, he admitted he was hesitant to talk to his co-workers about their at-risk behaviors.

"Out of all the people I spoke with – probably 20 or more – I only found two who actually seemed passionate about safety," Kurt said dejectedly. "One was a fairly new employee. The other had been working for about 15 years. Both said they were willing to shut the job down when they observed at-risk behaviors, even if their supervisor was pushing them for tonnage.

"When I asked why they were so motivated to work safely, one guy said his dad was an electrician at the mine and had taught the whole family to be safety-conscious, so it was second nature to him. The other employee said she had learned the hard way … she saw one of her buddies killed in an incident at the mine that could have been prevented. After that, she opted to go with her gut when it came to doing the job safely … and she didn't care what anybody else thought.

Kurt took a swig of his coffee. "So that's it in a nutshell. Lots of attitudes out there, huh?" As he finished reading through his list, he turned to a clean sheet on his notepad.

Sam put down his mug and leaned back. "Good work … and very impressive, too. You haven't wasted any time discovering *a person's attitude toward safety is a choice*, and there are four levels of commitment to safety you'll find on every job and in every person. If you'll let me borrow your pad, I'll draw them for you:

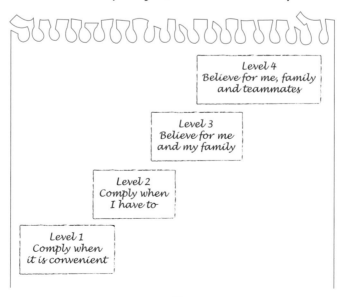

Level 4
Believe for me, family
and teammates

Level 3
Believe for me
and my family

Level 2
Comply when
I have to

Level 1
Comply when
it is convenient

Kurt looked closely at what Sam drew. Then he noticed something. "I think I get it. Level 1 and 2 say, 'comply' – meaning, 'I do it because I'm told, forced or paid to do it.' At Levels 3 and 4, the attitude changes to 'believe' – meaning, 'I make a conscious choice to practice safety and am totally committed to working in that mindset.' And when I reach Level 4, I'm demonstrating a true culture of safety."

"That's right," Sam said, nodding his head. "But I want to add one reminder – each of us is a blend of all four levels of commitment. So just because a worker demonstrates Level 4 most of the time, you need to expect he may revert to Level 1 when he doesn't know the potential danger."

Kurt studied the drawing closely. "I'm glad you mentioned that … so, Level 4 behaviors aren't constant?"

"Exactly … and here's another twist," Sam said. "Level 2 behaviors – complying with safety measures because we have to – will often look like Level 3 or Level 4.

"Does a person wear his personal protective equipment because the boss is around or because he truly believes in safety for himself and his co-workers?" Sam continued. "Ask yourself … why do you put your seat belt on when you drive? Do you do it because the police will stop you if you don't?"

"Well, I … er …." It was a question Kurt had to think about. "I'm trying to find the honest answer," he explained. "I've been using my seat belt so long, it's just a habit. When I first started, I used it because I knew it was the law, but when I read about people being killed when they weren't using their seat belts, it fueled my Level 4 mindset."

"Here's another one," Sam grinned, "and these are not trick questions.

Do you slow down when you see a police car sitting on the side of the road … or do you normally observe the speed limit?" He paused again as Kurt struggled to come up with an honest response.

"My point is this: You have to look beyond actions to determine the attitude causing the behavior. Those different attitudes impact the safety culture a company builds.

"Okay, now … I have a little review quiz for you. Do you remember how we defined 'culture' the last time we talked?" Sam asked.

"Isn't culture made up of group beliefs and behaviors that are passed on from one generation to another?" Kurt answered.

"Exactly," Sam said. "Now I want to expand on that further. ***We create our culture by what we demonstrate personally and by what we reward and tolerate in others.*** Think about what you've seen your company reward and tolerate."

Kurt was silent for several seconds before he responded. "I'm sure we must be rewarding some of the right behaviors … but, on the other hand, we're also missing a lot of the at-risk behaviors.

"For example, while I was in the mine dry, a person tossed a canned soft drink to a co-worker. At the same time, someone stood up to leave and almost got hit by the soda can.

"As another example, I was standing in the elevator at headquarters when the door began to close. A guy stuck his arm between the doors, just so he wouldn't have to wait for the next one. He was lucky enough to squeeze into the elevator before it started to move, but he could have lost fingers, a hand … or worse."

"And what about you – how did you demonstrate a personal commitment to safety?" Sam asked.

"Well, I spoke up when I observed at-risk behaviors. When the guy squeezed his way onto the elevator, I asked if he knew the risks of what he had done … but before he could answer, a woman standing next to me said she had just read about a doctor whose head was cut off when he got stuck in the door of a hospital elevator that went up to the next floor.

"I probably also surprised a lot of people in the break room. After I saw the guy toss the soda, I pointed out the risk involved," Kurt recounted. "Although the guy was embarrassed, he hadn't considered the possibility of his behavior causing injury, so I reminded him he'd been lucky this time, but then I explained the importance of safety, even during breaks."

Sam applauded. "That's a giant step, Kurt. Thanks for having the courage to speak up. If you'd taken the easy way out and stayed quiet, you would have perpetuated a culture that tolerates at-risk behaviors.

"Your safety conversations demonstrate your Level 4 commitment to safety," Sam beamed, "and in the strong safety culture you want to build, safe behaviors become a habit, a 'way of life,' for everyone because they're automatically reinforced.

"But, let me take a different route," the older man requested. "Have you or your wife ever tried going on a diet?"

Kurt chuckled, "You mean our annual New Year's resolution that lasts about two weeks?"

"About 10 years ago, my weight shot up to almost 300 pounds," Sam explained. "I tried a few diets without success and then asked my doctor for some of those diet pills you hear about. Well, he refused, saying what I needed to do was make healthy eating a way of life.

"Following a diet isn't a way of life. Neither is taking pills. The doctor told me I needed to relearn how to eat … so I could get back to the 225 I weighed for years."

Kurt had trouble visualizing the man sitting next to him ever weighing 300 pounds.

"The doctor helped me make simple changes in the way I ate and exercised … but they were changes I could live with on an ongoing basis. Needless to say, I didn't drop a whole lot of weight real fast. It took months, but I learned there's a real difference between being on a short-term diet versus healthy eating as a lifestyle. Once you make it a habit, you can keep it going over the long run."

"Okaayyy," Kurt said slowly. "So what does that have to do with establishing a safety culture?"

"Putting a new policy or procedure in place after an incident is just like taking diet pills after gaining 75 pounds," Sam explained. "Both help us feel we are doing something to solve the problem but neither creates long-term results.

"Remember the guy who talked about 'Safety is Our Number One Priority'? He said the company emphasized that program until tonnage levels dropped and then production replaced safety as a priority."

Sam shook his finger as he continued. "These are the cold, hard facts. Just like dieting usually doesn't result in permanent weight loss, policies alone cannot guarantee a totally safe workplace … no matter how hard we try."

"So, a strong safety culture begins when we *Make Safety a HABIT*™?" Kurt wondered.

"A habit you practice every minute of the day," Sam said. "Yes, that's a good first step and, speaking of steps, do you know what a step-change is?"

"Only if you're talking about country-western dancing," Kurt laughed.

"No, 'Tex,' I'm talking about a step-change in safety," Sam said with a smile. "The mining industry has improved its safety performance, thanks to engineering, technology and legislation.

"Looking back as far as 1907, when U.S. mines lost 3,242 miners, our industry was considered one of the deadliest. People in our industry were viewed as hard-working individuals, swinging picks and shovels. Because everybody knew mining was dangerous, we simply accepted 'accidents will happen.'

"Our first real steps in improving safety began about that same time, through cooperation between mining companies, labor and the government," Sam continued. "For example, the Bureau of Mines was created in 1910 following the Monogah tragedy and, gradually, there were more mine safety standards – like the Federal Coal Mine Safety Act of 1952.

"At that point, geophysical and geological maps and information were becoming more dependable and specific areas could be targeted for exploration. In other words, miners were no longer in the dark as they moved from one level to the next. More sophisticated water pumps were developed to displace ground water. Electricity replaced steam and water energy to run compressors for the drills," Sam continued.

"As mining technology improved, companies expected fewer people would get injured as a result … and this did reduce injuries and fatalities. But, over time, people became complacent with the new equipment, and the opportunities to engineer safety became fewer.

"Once our industry realized technology and engineering still didn't prevent incidents from occurring, we saw legislation continue to evolve in an effort to improve safety. New laws, like the Federal Mine Safety and Health Act of 1977, were put into effect, placing coal mines, metal and nonmetal mines under a single law and moved enforcement to the Mine Safety and Health Administration (MSHA).

"At the same time, companies wrote hundreds of policies, and the government expected fewer people would get injured as a result of increased regulation. Unfortunately, it didn't prevent disasters from continuing … even now. I know you followed the two U.S. mine disasters in 2006. In the first, an explosion killed 12 miners in West Virginia, which was followed by another that killed five people in Kentucky just a few months later. How many does that make?" Sam asked grimly.

"That's 17 lives lost." Kurt shook his head and sat quietly, digesting this information.

"Keep in mind, while those numbers are gut-wrenching, they don't even take into account the number of miners killed in South America, China and the former Soviet Union that same year," Sam said quietly.

"It's hard for me to wrap my mind around this because I can't imagine what it would do to Jessica and Shannon if a stranger knocked on our door to tell them I had been killed. And I know, regardless of what country the incident may have occurred, the crippling pain of losing a loved one feels the same." Kurt sighed.

"Because of the incidents that occurred in the United States in June 2006, President George W. Bush signed the Mine Improvement and New Emergency Response (MINER) Act into law," Sam said.

"It was the most significant mine safety legislation in 30 years to improve mine safety. It also called for the modernization of safety practices and development of enhanced communication technology," he went on, "and was passed so miners could return home safely to their families at the end of every shift. Sound familiar?"

Kurt nodded.

"Then, in 2007, there was a mine collapse in the U.S. that killed six miners and three rescuers," Sam continued, "Subsequent investigations of these and other mining disasters around the globe always find the same thing: not following procedures, inadequate equipment, lack of proper training and preparedness. So, even today, when mines have the best equipment and technology and are regulated by all those laws, policies and procedures, safety still comes down to people."

"Did any good come out of all the laws, investigations and regulations?" Kurt asked as he lowered his head and combed his fingers through his short brown hair.

"Absolutely," Sam responded. "It ushered in the 'Era of Behavior-based Safety.' Don't get me wrong, the work is still hard and dangerous and, unfortunately, incidents still happen, but now it is the 'individual' who has to expect not to get injured. You see, creating a safe work environment is a personal issue, not only a corporate one."

"I remember the last time we met, you said, 'We get the level of safety we expect,'" Kurt said thoughtfully.

"You've got a good memory," Sam complimented. "Early on in the mining industry's history, it was the company that expected to improve safety ...."

Kurt completed the thought, "... and then governments and labor unions expected it ...."

"Oh, the unions still push hard for workplace safety," Sam interrupted, "and there's no better way to demonstrate 'brotherhood' than watching out for the safety of a co-worker."

"That's true," responded Kurt. "But to really get people to watch out for each other, we have to stop looking for someone to 'blame' if an incident does occur."

"What we've learned is that legislation, technology and policies alone don't eliminate incidents. ***Providing the 'tools' necessary for a safe work environment is a corporate responsibility, but creating a culture of safety is a personal responsibility, as well as a corporate one.*** The critical step in improving mine safety depends on individuals expecting zero incidents. Take the military – a huge organization – for example," Sam continued. "Have you heard how much emphasis they're putting on reducing personnel injuries and incidents?"

"Sure, I just read an article that despite all the state-of-the-art equipment and lots of regulations, incident rates are near an all-time high. But look how dangerous their environment is," Kurt replied.

"No one would argue the risks associated with being in a 'hostile' environment," Sam agreed, "but the majority of incidents taking place are non-combat related.

"The military is taking steps to reduce these incidents through implementing new regulations and technologies, but just like the mining industry evolved from the 'Era of Death' to the 'Era of Behavior-based Safety,' reducing at-risk behavior and eliminating incidents requires a step-change in the industry's culture, coming to a point where individuals expect not to get injured."

"Sam, you've given me a lot to think about … and you've helped me make some sense of what I've been seeing and hearing over the past two weeks." Kurt paused to chuckle. "Talk about a fast track. I'm going as fast as I can, but it feels like I've barely made it out of the starting gate … and with that 120-day deadline looming large, the finish line is still miles away."

Sam nodded his approval and reached over to tap Kurt's head. "They've got it here, son. Now, you've got to get them to feel it here," said the older man, tapping his chest.

# MINER'S LAMP

**ESSENTIAL CONCEPTS:**

✦ Everything we do carries an element of risk … and survival depends on how well we manage those elements of risk.

✦ Each of us chooses our attitude toward safety.

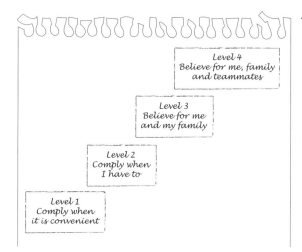

✦ Levels of commitment to safety: Everyone is a blend of these various levels. The question becomes "Which level of commitment do we demonstrate most frequently?"

✦ We create our culture by what we demonstrate personally and by what we reward and tolerate in others.

✦ A strong safety culture begins when we *Make Safety a HABIT*™.

✦ Brotherhood means watching out for the safety of co-workers.

✦ Take the emphasis off blaming someone if an incident does occur.

✦ Providing the 'tools' necessary for a safe work environment is a corporate responsibility. Creating a culture of safety is a personal responsibility, as well as a corporate one.

# Accentuating the Positive — As Easy as ABC

As Kurt continued to visit the company's various locations around the world, he began to realize that establishing a strong culture of safety for the entire company would be the ultimate test of his career.

To create a strong safety culture, poor safety habits would have to be identified and set apart from proper practices. In most cases, that would mean changing individual behaviors.

Kurt decided the first step would be to develop a process that enabled employees to make a personal commitment to work safely.

It was clear to the new director of safety: His company, like many others, had spent a lot of money and effort initiating numerous safety programs. However, very little time had been spent on follow-up and reinforcement.

"How can you accomplish measurable results when you spend the majority of your time implementing a new program?" Kurt wondered as he went through the large stack of folders he had brought home that evening.

Long before his alarm went off the next morning, Kurt's phone rang.

Fumbling for the receiver, Kurt managed a hoarse hello.

"Kurt, it's Tom Montano in Chile. Sorry to wake you, but I'm afraid I have some bad news."

Kurt sat up.

"John Sullivan's been injured in an automobile accident near Antofagasta," Montano continued. "They've taken him to the Regional Hospital here. I don't know how bad his injuries are. They're trying to stabilize him now."

Kurt was now wide awake. "I'll get down there as soon as I can," he said. "How's Theresa doing?"

Hearing her friend's name, Jessica sat up to listen.

"Oh, she's pretty shook up," came the reply. "We all are."

"Tell her I'm on my way and Jessica and I have both of them in our thoughts."

"Will do," Montano said. "Let me know your arrival time and I'll send a driver."

"Sure thing," Kurt said, hanging up the phone.

"How bad is it?" Jessica asked gently.

"Don't know, but bad enough for John to be in the hospital after a car wreck," Kurt replied. "I'll have to get a flight out as soon as I can."

"Why don't you jump in the shower while I start packing your bag?" Jessica offered.

"Not before I have a hug," her husband took her into his arms. "I love you so much … and I'm praying John is going to be okay."

"Poor Theresa," Jessica whispered in her husband's ear. "John is her rock."

"I know. I know," Kurt answered.

It was after 9:00 that morning when Kurt finalized arrangements for his flight to Chile.

"Kurt," Sam's familiar voice greeted him. "Just wanted to call about our meeting this week."

"Sam! I'm glad you called. I'm on my way to the airport. There's been a car crash in Chile and I need to get down there … but hey, how are you at spur-of-the-moment trips? I think your safety expertise could be a real plus on this one."

"I keep my passport updated," Sam said. "I could be packed and at the airport in an hour."

"Let me clear it with my boss."

After reaching altitude, the drone of the plane's engine settled into a steady rhythm. Putting down his newspaper, Kurt turned to Sam. "I've got to confess, I'm really worried about John. He's a good man and valuable to the company, but more than that, his wife and son rely on John to make their worlds go round." Kurt remembered the times he had spent with John and grew quiet.

"I went to the office and found out a few more details about the incident before coming to the airport," Kurt explained. "As I listened to what happened, I found myself looking at the incident from a whole different viewpoint," he continued.

Sam sat quietly, allowing Kurt to talk as much as he wanted about his friend and the crash.

"Three people from our Antofagasta office had spent the evening at a client reception near El Cobre Gigante Mine, one of the world's largest copper mines."

"Know it well," Sam nodded. "I believe it could be considered the largest open pit operation in the world."

"During the party their driver became too ill to drive, so in their hurry to get back to town, the guys – including John – decided to drive themselves," Kurt continued.

"Montano said John was thrown from the car because he wasn't wearing a seatbelt … which is unbelievable. John is such a stickler for safety. He's not only that way at work, he's that way at home and with his family.

"Perhaps I'm trying to over-analyze the crash because I'm beginning to recognize people's at-risk behaviors," the young director concluded.

"That's definitely a good first step," Sam said, resting his elbow on the arm rest between them. "Your perspective and awareness are definitely changing how you look at other people. Remember though, for real change to occur, behavior has to change, yours included."

"What do you mean?" Kurt asked.

"You've probably flown on airplanes a lot in your career, so much so that you unconsciously put on your seatbelt when you sit down. But let me ask you, where are the life jackets located?" Sam was watching Kurt closely.

"Underneath my seat, and my seat cushion can be used as a flotation device," Kurt said, mimicking a flight attendant.

"On this airplane, the life jackets are *between* the seats," Sam explained. "Imagine trying to figure that out in a smoke-filled cabin."

"I guess I should have listened to the flight attendant a little closer. Boy, do I feel like a Level One," Kurt said, putting his newspaper in the seat pocket in front of him.

"Or, what about when you check into a hotel. Do you ever look to see where the emergency exits are located and make sure they're not obstructed or chained closed?"

Kurt shook his head. "And I'm supposed to help our company create a strong safety culture???"

Sam chuckled. "You are definitely not a lost cause, but in order to maintain a clear vision of safety, you have to mentally practice identifying your own at-risk behaviors.

"Before we talk about the next step in building a culture of safety, I want to show you some photographs." The older man unzipped his bag and retrieved a small photo album. "These photos are several years old, but they make a point."

As he looked through the album, Kurt saw a toddler he estimated to be about a year old. In the first shot, she was standing with Sam holding her hands above her head as she took a clumsy step. In the second, Sam had let go of her hands.

The third shot showed the little girl taking a step on her own. Successive shots showed her trying again and then falling into waiting arms. In the final shot, she was sitting in Sam's lap, enjoying a cookie.

"She's cute," Kurt said, handing back the album. "I'm assuming she's your granddaughter."

"Yes." Sam nodded, smiling. "These aren't just proud grandpa shots. I brought them along because they illustrate something you need to know."

"Ookaaay," Kurt said slowly, feeling as though he may have, once again, missed the obvious.

"It's pretty basic, really," Sam said, replacing the album into his bag. "Those photographs illustrate the 'ABC's of performance,' a key point in changing behaviors. In the first photograph, I stood Erika up and held her hands over her head to keep her from falling. I call that the 'Activator' – what I needed to do before I could expect Erika to take her first step and to give her confidence she could do it.

"In the next picture, you saw her take a step by herself – that's the 'Behavior' I wanted. In the final shot, you saw the 'Consequence' – the positive feedback she received from me – a hug and a cookie."

Kurt smiled, remembering the similar process he and Jessica had used when Shannon was first learning to walk ... too many years ago.

"Of course, building a strong safety culture isn't as simple as offering a person a cookie if they do what you want them to do, but the principle is the same: **A**ctivator-**B**ehavior-**C**onsequence," Sam continued.

"I didn't realize it before, but I used the ABC's every day when I was in operations," Kurt recalled. "It started by making sure my team had clear goals, then I checked on them during the job to see how they were progressing and, finally, I always followed up to be sure they clearly understood the result of their efforts and shared my feeling of accomplishment."

Kurt looked out the window as he thought about previous jobs he had done. "I also found my team liked to be 'caught doing something right,' which was a concept I learned at a seminar several years ago. 'Accentuating the positive' seemed to motivate every member of the team, regardless of how long they had been with the company."

"That's because responding to positive reinforcement – like Erika and the cookie – is a human characteristic," Sam replied. "To give you an example, several months after my granddaughter was born, her big brother Kevin was having a hard time going from being the only child, and the center of attention, to being Erika's big brother.

"It didn't take him long to figure out if he couldn't get attention one way, he would get it another – like writing on the walls or putting rocks down the toilet. He didn't care if the attention received was negative ... all that mattered was that the focus was on him.

"My daughter quickly decided to teach him the 'ABC's' at an early age. She started to redirect, or 'activate,' Kevin's energy into another activity, like coloring on a piece of paper or going outside and playing on the swing set, which changed his 'behavior' and resulted in a positive 'consequence'."

Again, Kurt thought about what he and Sam had discussed previously. It was all starting to make sense. "Now I understand how important the ABC's are in creating the type of culture we need to reduce our incident rates."

Sam smiled at his young friend's progress. "Yes, but keep in mind, while the ABC's will help change behavior, it must be clear that those changes will result in the culture you are trying to create … and let me tell you what I mean by that.

"As you know, in underground mines, the longwall mining process makes a deafening noise, so somebody came up with the idea of using a blinking light to signal when the shearing machine began moving over the face of the coal.

"When the light was blinking, the miners knew to stay out of the path of the machine," Sam continued his story. "On one shift, the light didn't come on when it was supposed to … so one of the miners, unknowingly, stepped in the path of the machine and was badly hurt.

"On that particular day, as it turned out, the light bulb had burned out.

"Unfortunately, having everyone focus on the light to make decisions created the wrong behavior," Sam concluded, "and that resulted in the same consequence they were trying to avoid."

"I know what you mean about the solution sometimes creating the behavior you are trying to change," Kurt nodded. "Because I drive a company car, I had to attend a defensive driving course. I was taught things like how to get out of a spin, backing up quickly and emergency braking. When I got out of the course, I thought I was even more invincible."

"You're right," replied Sam. "Teaching someone how to get out of a spin without first addressing the choices they made that put them in the spin is like closing the gate after the horse is out. It's great if a person knows how to handle a dangerous situation, but I'd ask whether it was necessary for them to be at risk in the first place."

Kurt nodded his agreement, "Just like the blinking light in the mine."

"Ladies and gentlemen." The pilot's voice interrupted from the aircraft's intercom. "We'll be landing at Aeropuerto Internacional Cerro Moreno in about an hour."

"This afternoon has gone by more quickly than I anticipated," Kurt said, taking a deep breath and letting it out slowly. "When we land, I want to go directly to the hospital. I need to find out how John and his family are doing. I'll have to admit, this whole thing has torn me up."

"Incidents and injuries affect many more than just those who were physically hurt. It's like dropping a pebble in the water and watching the circles spread across the entire pond," Sam said, almost in a whisper.

"Your being here for John and his family is a good thing. It will motivate him to get better, and motivate us to make sure it doesn't happen to anyone else in the company." Sam's voice was reassuring.

# MINER'S LAMP

## ESSENTIAL CONCEPTS:

✦ For real change to occur, behavior has to change …
ours included.

✦ To maintain a clear vision of safety, each of us has to
mentally practice identifying our own at-risk behaviors.

✦ The ABC's of Performance: **A**ctivator-**B**ehavior-
**C**onsequence. Clearly communicate the goal you expect,
follow up to see how they are progressing and, at the end,
be sure they see the result of their efforts.

✦ Noticing when people do something right – or "accentuating
the positive" – is a strong motivator because responding to
positive reinforcement is a human characteristic.

✦ To change a behavior, redirect the person to a different
goal and provide a positive consequence when he or she
achieves it.

✦ Incidents and injuries affect many more people than just
those who were physically hurt – much like the ever-widening
ripples caused by dropping a pebble in the water.

# HUMAN NATURE IN A HIGH-RISK ENVIRONMENT

It had been unseasonably warm in Antofagasta. As the plane landed, Kurt and Sam commented about the hazy clouds that almost met the hilltops outlining the small airport.

John had been driving the night of the crash. After attending the client reception near Cerro Colosa and the El Cobre Gigante mine, he and two co-workers were driving home when John swerved to miss something moving on the road. The car had spun out of control, causing the vehicle to leave the roadway and roll into a deep gully.

Tom Montano provided some of the details as the trio left the airport, heading for the hospital in the city's center. "John's in pretty bad shape … two broken legs," Tom began, "but the doctors believe he is out of danger. The first few hours after the crash were touch and go because of internal bleeding, but surgery seems to have corrected those problems."

"That's good to hear," Kurt said, obviously relieved.

"As an expatriate myself, I'm surprised John was driving," Sam commented, knowing local drivers usually drove ex-pats in most of the company's international operations.

"Apparently the driver had been ill all day and, during the course of the evening, his stomach pains grew worse," Montano said. "You know how John is … he always wants to help. He released the driver for the night and planned to call another driver. When no one was available, John offered to drive."

"But, why was he the only one thrown from the vehicle?" Kurt wanted to know.

By now, they had pulled into a parking space near what appeared to be a relatively new building. Montano grimaced before answering. "As I mentioned on the phone, I don't think he was wearing a seatbelt. The others were."

Kurt shook his head in disbelief. John was one of the most safety-conscious people he had ever known. Surely he hadn't overlooked something as simple as fastening a safety belt.

"All right if we leave our stuff here?" Sam wondered out loud as he unbuckled his own seat belt and climbed out of the car.

"The driver is going to stay with the car," Montano said, "and our visit is going to have to be a short one. Visiting hours are over in 15 minutes … and, believe me, they're strictly enforced."

John's wife, Theresa, saw the three men coming down the long hall and met them halfway. "John's been sleeping most of the day," she said, giving Kurt a big hug as she struggled to maintain her composure. "But he'll be so happy to see you, even with all the medication they're giving him."

Kurt took a moment to introduce Theresa to Sam, who, along with Montano, excused himself to the waiting room around the corner.

As Kurt followed Theresa to her husband's bedside, he remembered her as a beautiful woman with unforgettable eyes. Today her face was lined with worry and her eyes dulled by lack of sleep.

John's room was dark, except for a dim light over the hospital bed where lines and pulleys kept John's legs elevated in their heavy casts. His face was swollen, scraped and cut in several places. A large gash, now stitched, traveled well into his hairline.

"John, Kurt is here," Theresa whispered and patted her husband's arm to waken him.

The man in the hospital bed opened his eyes. "Hiya, Mate," his Australian accent clearly evident despite his condition. "Did a pretty good job of getting you down here."

"What are you doing in bed, man? You're not due a vacation for months," Kurt joked.

"Some vacation," John said, attempting to smile.

"I hear you're going to make it," Kurt reassured, as he reached to touch his friend's arm. "Keep up the good work … and try not to give your nurses a hard time."

The man in the bed nodded, closed his eyes and dozed off from the drugs he had been given for pain.

"Is Ethan here?" Kurt asked as he and Theresa stepped back into the hall.

"I told him to stay at school," she replied. "He's getting ready for first-quarter exams and, besides, what can he do?"

"He could be here to support his mother … and his dad," Kurt answered, knowing full well Theresa's independence wouldn't allow her son to miss classes.

"I'll be fine," Theresa said. "We talk every few hours, so he's keeping up with what's going on. I've hired a private nurse to keep a close eye on John, so I think I'll go home tonight … sleep in my own bed."

Kurt gave her another hug. "I'm staying at the Radisson," he said, holding Theresa at arm's length. "I also want you to take my mobile number. I expect you to let me know if you need anything," he added, scribbling his number on a piece of paper he had pulled from a small pad in his pocket.

"Thank you for being here, Kurt," she said, squeezing his arm before returning to kiss her husband goodnight.

✦ ✦ ✦ ✦ ✦

After Kurt had spent time with the two other men who had been riding with John the night of the wreck, he and Sam sat down for a late dinner.

"I've known John for years," Kurt was saying. "I've worked with him and I just cannot believe he took the risk of getting behind the wheel without being that familiar with the road … or the automobile he was driving. It's so out of character for him."

Sam put down his menu. "Could be his natural tolerance of risk coming into play."

"What do you mean?" asked Kurt, trying to decide between camarones and Cacho de Cabra.

"We naturally tolerate some risks because we don't even notice they exist. We may not be aware something could be potentially dangerous. In John's case, had he ever been on that particular road before? Was he aware of the condition of the road or the winding stretch where the incident occurred?

"In other situations, we become complacent because we've done something so many times without a problem, we take it for granted nothing will happen the next time we do the same thing. John may have thought, 'I'm a safe driver and never been in a crash so I'm the best one to handle this.'

"Finally, there are some people – probably not John – but there are folks who actually enjoy the thrill of taking risks, especially when it gets them noticed. They get a 'rush' when they take chances and receive praise."

"So risk tolerance should always be factored into the equation when you're looking at an incident and its causes?" Kurt asked, closing his menu.

"That's right ... ***most injuries and incidents are the result of people's natural risk tolerance***, which could be impacted by lots of things, including the country they live in. But more importantly, before starting, or anytime there is a change during the task, a person should factor in their risk tolerance by asking themselves three questions," Sam emphasized as he began writing on a napkin.

1. Am I aware of all the risks associated with this task?

2. Have I become complacent as a result of doing this task many times before?

3. Have I allowed my desire for a thrill or praise to impact the way I will conduct this task?

"Montano said something about rushing to get home before midnight because of a conference call scheduled for early the next morning. That still doesn't tell me why John would take the risks," said Kurt, rubbing the fatigue from his eyes, "or why the other guys wouldn't try to stop him."

"Those all are good questions," Sam said, "but I want to try to help you get at the basics here."

"Okay, shoot."

"First of all, you need to realize thousands of incident investigations – like the one you're doing now – are conducted every day ... after someone is hurt. Now that John is in the hospital, we look at all the variables that lined up prior to the incident occurring. But chances are, those same variables are not going to line up again in exactly the same way as they did before.

"We need to teach people how to observe those variables or risks and, more importantly, how to prevent them from lining up in such a way as to cause an incident," the older man added.

A waiter interrupted Sam to take their orders. Once the waiter left the table, Kurt asked Sam, "Do I hear you saying people get hurt because they don't make conscious choices about how not to get hurt?"

"That's correct," Sam said. "You may assess the risks when you decide, 'I'm not going to get hurt,' but you still consciously need to think through, 'how' am I going to stay safe despite the potential risks? It's that conscious thought – that conversation, whether with yourself or your team – that's key."

"And that conversation can take place anywhere, anytime, 24/7," Kurt replied as the waiter reappeared with their dinner. "Now let's enjoy this feast before we both fall asleep."

Before going to bed, Kurt made a call to Montano, asking if he could see the wrecked automobile the next day. Then he called Sam's room.

"I'm going to look at the car first thing tomorrow," Kurt explained. "Want to go?"

"If it will work into your schedule, why not just drop me at the company office on your way?" Sam suggested. "I'd like to spend some time talking to the people there."

"Sounds like a plan," Kurt responded. "Montano will pick us up at 7:00. I'll see you in the morning."

The car appeared to be a total loss as Kurt walked around the dusty, white sedan. One tire was blown out, windows were smashed and the frame was badly bent. Then something caught his eye. The driver's seat belt was buckled and the left portion of the belt had been ripped from its bolted position on the floor.

A wave of relief flooded Kurt's thoughts. "I knew John wouldn't drive without a seat belt," he said to himself, "and that tire … could it have blown, causing the car to go out of control?"

But what remained of the wrecked vehicle still didn't answer his question about why John decided to risk driving that night.

Sam's words from the night before returned. "We have to consciously recognize the hazards."

"But, isn't it possible that everything around us is a hazard?" he said aloud.

"What?" Montano asked.

"Oh … sorry! When you're thinking about doing things safely, would it be possible for everything around us to be a hazard?" Kurt repeated.

"Hadn't thought about it like that before," Montano replied. "It's possible, I guess … like that rock over there?"

"Right. **A hazard is anything that has the potential to contribute to an incident taking place**, so that rock is a hazard," Kurt explained, "but because hazards exist all around us, we have to continually assess risks to prioritize and focus on those hazards that have a greater likelihood of contributing to an incident, as well as its severity.

"Let me put it this way – as long as the rock is over there and I'm over here, the likelihood that rock will contribute to an incident is very low. But, if that same rock were close to me – maybe a portion of it is hidden beneath the dirt – the likelihood of me kicking, or tripping over it increases significantly."

"Now that we're talking about it, I probably wouldn't have thought about that rock being a hazard," Montano said.

"Maybe not consciously, but our five senses – sight, hearing, touch, smell and taste – are continually processing the environment around us for potential danger." Kirk took out a piece of paper and began writing as he continued his thought. "We need to *Make Safety a HABIT*™

by raising it to a conscious level, here, I'll draw something I've come up with."

*H*azard

*A*ssessment

*B*efore

*I*nitiating

*T*ask™

"The first step is to ask ourselves, 'What around us has the *potential* to cause an incident?' And remember, there are hazards we don't even recognize as potential dangers because we are unaware, have become complacent, or are looking for a thrill or praise, also known as 'our natural risk tolerance.'

"The second step in the process is to ask ourselves, 'What is the *likelihood* the hazard will contribute to an incident?' But, just like the first step, my natural risk tolerance may cause me to underestimate the hazard."

Montano took a moment. "So, ***managing our safety starts by consciously recognizing the hazards*** and then determining the likelihood of an incident occurring, in one of three ways:

**Remote** – It is very unlikely it will happen.

**Possible** – There is a chance of it happening but it's not inevitable.

**Probable** – It's likely to happen or inevitable.

"You've got it," Kurt said. "Now, as I look at this wreck, something else occurs to me that I'll share with you. ***Risk assessment is driven by the task, not by the people doing the task.***"

Montano looked puzzled.

"Let me explain it this way," Kurt offered. "Let's say you're an experienced driver, so you may feel the task of driving is not a risk to you because you know how to drive. But, my point is, risk is based on the potential hazards associated with the task itself, not the risk relative to you or how many years you've been doing the task.

"Your experience helps reduce the hazards associated with the task – in this case, driving – and lessens the likelihood and severity of an incident taking place," Kurt continued.

"In the case of John's crash, I think the incident that night might have happened no matter who was driving," he went on. "Visibility, familiarity with the road or the potential of a tire blowing out are a few of the hazards that existed, regardless of who was driving. The problem was, because of his natural risk tolerance, John didn't do anything to reduce any of the hazards that existed.

"What he should have done was think, 'What task – driving – am I about to do? What are the potential hazards? What's the likelihood of an incident occurring? How severe could the incident be if it were to occur? How can I reduce those hazards that exist?'"

"What if John was unsure about any of the answers?" Montano asked.

"If he was unsure, or something in his gut told him something wasn't quite right, he shouldn't have gotten behind the wheel," Kurt responded, kicking a small pebble out of the way.

Back at the office, Kurt briefed Sam on his findings.

"Well, you've certainly had a productive morning," Sam said.

Kurt was ready to get right to his questions. "If a person's natural risk tolerance, or at-risk behavior, impacts their ability to do a task safely, who is responsible for calling it to their attention?"

He paused and looked up. "Take John as an example. He was so eager to get the job done – in this case, get home and get some sleep – he didn't think about the risks associated with driving. However, there were two other people in the car …."

"Remember," Sam interrupted, "in a strong safety culture, everyone is responsible for speaking up when they observe a person performing an at-risk behavior, regardless of the reasons why or the person's level of seniority in the company."

"I realize that, Sam. What I meant was, there were two other people in the car who could have said something, but why didn't they?" Kurt replied.

"Many times the 'culture' prevents people from speaking up because they don't know what to say or how to say it … or they're afraid to say it."

"What do you mean by the word 'culture'?" Kurt wanted to know.

"Well, in many cases, a national employee may feel uncomfortable speaking up to an expatriate, which can be a 'cultural' barrier. Other times, a subordinate may have difficulty speaking up to a supervisor, but either case can tell us something about the company's culture.

"The key is to create a level of trust that allows people to speak up," Sam continued. Everyone, especially supervisors, has to learn **when it comes to safety, disagreement does not mean disrespect.**"

"Talk about a culture change …" Kurt said, closing his notebook and following Sam through the door and back to their waiting car.

 **MINER'S LAMP**

**DEFINITIONS:**

**Natural tolerance for risk:** Individuals naturally tolerate some risk primarily for three reasons:

1. **Unaware:** A person doesn't even know the hazards exist ... he isn't aware something could be dangerous.

2. **Complacency:** An individual becomes complacent because he's done something so many times without a problem, he takes it for granted nothing will happen the next time he does the same thing.

3. **Thrill seekers:** These individuals actually enjoy the thrill of taking risks. They get a 'rush' when they take chances or receive praise.

4. **Hazard:** Anything that has the potential to contribute to an incident taking place.

5. *Make Safety a HABIT*™
   *H*azard
   *A*ssessment
   *B*efore
   *I*nitiating
   *T*ask™

**ESSENTIAL CONCEPTS:**

✦ Most injuries and incidents are the result of people's natural risk tolerance.

✦ Before starting a task, we can reduce our risk tolerance by answering these three questions:

1. Am I aware of all the risks associated with this task?
2. Have I become complacent as a result of doing this task many times before?
3. Have I allowed my desire for a thrill to impact the way I will conduct this task?

✦ People get hurt because they don't make conscious choices about how not to get hurt.

✦ In addition to deciding "I'm not going to get hurt," we still consciously need to think through, *how* am I going to stay safe, despite the potential risks? Whether talking to ourselves or our team, this conversation is the key to our safety.

✦ Managing our safety starts when we consciously *Make Safety a HABIT*™ … and realize everything around us has the potential to contribute to an incident.

✦ Risk assessment is driven by the task, not by the people doing the task.

✦ In a strong safety culture, everyone is accountable for speaking up when they observe a person performing an at-risk behavior.

✦ A *culture* may prevent someone from speaking up because they don't know what to say or how to say it. Therefore, a culture of safety creates a level of trust that encourages people to speak up.

✦ When it comes to safety, disagreement does not mean disrespect.

# THE BASIS OF THE *HABIT*™ CONVERSATION

The early morning breeze revitalized Kurt as he walked up the hospital steps.

His daily visits seemed to be helping speed John's recovery. As Kurt entered the room, John sat up with help from the metal bar hanging overhead.

"You still here?"

"I'm a bit of a captive audience, wouldn't you say?" John shot back.

"Well, I didn't come to see your ugly face anyway. Where's Theresa?"

"Oh, she's talking to the doctor about my physical therapy. It begins this afternoon," John announced, unable to hide his excitement. "The doctor let me know it'll be a long road to recovery. From here I'll go to a rehabilitation center for a month, but I may make it out of there before the holidays …."

Kurt didn't want to dampen John's spirit, but his job required him to talk with his friend, sooner or later. "So, how do you feel about discussing the wreck?" he asked.

"I'll do my best, Mate. What do you want to know?" John asked, grimacing.

"I've looked over the incident report, but I want you to tell me what happened," Kurt said, looking through his papers.

Straightening his back, John began. "About 10:30 p.m., I decided it was time to head home, but my driver had become sick earlier in the evening and I released him to go home, assuming I could easily call for another driver.

"But when I couldn't find a driver, and realized I was the only one who hadn't had anything stronger than lemonade to drink that night, I decided to drive. The other two hopped in the back seat and promptly fell asleep.

"We had been traveling about 10 minutes and sand was blowing, so I slowed down and literally crept around the turns. All of a sudden something appeared ahead of me – maybe an animal – I don't know. I veered to the right, trying to avoid whatever it was and ended up going off the road. I was trying to do the right thing … I …. "

Kurt looked squarely at his friend. "It's not about blaming you. The issue is how could you have gotten home safely?

"I realize the circumstances changed … you didn't go to the party planning to drive home … but you know it's against company policy for an ex-pat to drive in Chile," Kurt continued. "Another issue is the condition of the vehicle. Did you know anything about the car before getting behind the wheel?"

"Like what? A late model sedan … I think it had a half tank of gas and was a little dusty from our trip across the desert, but that's about all," John recounted.

"When I went out to look at the car, I found the seatbelt had ripped from its mooring," Kurt said. "Overall, the seatbelt was in pretty bad shape, just waiting for the impact of a crash to send the driver flying."

John was silent for a moment. "I'll admit, my judgment was not the best," he finally managed, "but none of us could come up with a faster way to get home, so I was behind the wheel by default … and – please understand, Mate, I'm not making excuses."

"So looking back, how much time did you really save?" Kurt let the question hang in the air. "I know you're a good driver and probably didn't think there were any risks, but you also didn't decide how you *weren't* going to get hurt."

"So, how does that work?" John asked. "Of course hindsight is 20/20, but it would be good to know for future reference."

Kurt was pleased with John's response. "I'm glad you asked that question. As I learn more about developing a culture of safety, I'm finding we need to place more emphasis on assessing the risks of everything we do … before we do them, whether it's something like driving, how we sit at our desks, or the way we go up and down stairs.

"It's a simple process, really," Kurt went on. "Before we start a task, like you driving that night, we need to *Make Safety a HABIT™* and ask ourselves three questions:

1. **What am I doing?** I'm driving a car back to Antofagasta.

2. **What might be hazardous about what I'm doing?** I'm not familiar with this vehicle or road. Sometimes periodic dust

storms limit visibility or late-night humidity can create a slick roadway.

3. **What can I do to reduce those hazards?** Your best answer would have been, "We need to call another driver to come out and pick us up, someone who knows this vehicle, the road, and knows how to drive in the desert."

"The point is this: ***Risk assessing is consciously and purposefully deciding how we are not going to get hurt.***"

"So, is it possible to eliminate all risks?" John asked.

"Unfortunately, not," Kurt responded. "But, you bring up a good point. ***Risk is determined by the probability of an incident occurring, given the associated hazards***, and a hazard is anything that has the potential to contribute to an incident taking place.

"Therefore, the level of risk a person faces depends on the presence or absence of hazards," he continued. "To put it simply, ***the more hazards we can eliminate, the lower the risk.***

"It does sound pretty simple," John said. "And something anyone can – I mean everyone – should do."

"Well, I'd better be going. I have work to do and people to see," Kurt said as he gave his friend's arm a reassuring squeeze. "I'll be flying back to the States tomorrow, but I'll stop in on my way to the airport."

After lunch, Kurt and Sam were on their way to El Cobre Gigante to attend safety meetings. They asked Tom Montano to come along in case they needed an interpreter.

When they arrived, Guillermo, one of the mine's supervisors, welcomed them warmly and began the tour. As they walked around, Sam noticed a man on the conveyor line, shoveling ore spillage onto a moving conveyer belt. But, what really caught his eye was the man's safety vest was unzipped … and every time he swung the shovel toward the belt line, the loose vest came alarmingly close to being caught in the belt roller.

"Guillermo, do you mind if I try to talk with one of your people for a minute?" Sam asked.

"Sure, is there a problem?" Guillermo asked, looking around.

"Just a small one, but I want to make sure it doesn't become a bigger one," Sam said walking over to the belt man. "Hello, can I talk with you for a few minutes?" Sam asked to see if the man spoke English.

"Sí señor," the worker agreed, stepping away from the conveyor and leaning his shovel against a sign.

Sam introduced himself and Montano. "I observed you shoveling, and I'm real pleased to see you have your safety gear on and you're not using a D-handled shovel. There's something that concerns me about your safety, though. Do you know what it might be?"

"I guess it's pretty slippery where I am working," the belt man said, looking around to see who was watching.

"Do you normally wear a reflective safety vest?" Sam explored a little further.

"Of course. It is required when you are on mine property," came the reply.

"I noticed your vest is unzipped and opens every time you swing your shovel toward the belt," Sam continued.

"Oh, sí," the belt man responded. "It is very hot today and I unzipped the vest to cool off."

"It is hot," Sam agreed, "but what's the worst thing that could happen if your vest got caught in the conveyor roller?"

The man was thoughtful. "Well, I guess I could get hurt."

"Like if the vest got caught and it pulled you into the moving conveyor," Sam pushed harder.

"I could be hurt bad … even killed, but I'm real careful and that's never happened before," he answered, trying to reassure the man standing in front of him.

Seeming to change subjects, Sam asked, "Do you have a wife and kids at home?"

"Yes, a wife and four children … three boys and a girl."

"You must be very proud," Sam smiled. "But, what would happen to them if you were hurt and couldn't work anymore?" Sam asked, making sure the conversation stayed on track.

"It would be really bad, because we take care of my wife's parents, too," came the serious reply.

"Is there something you could do to make your work by this conveyor belt safer?" Sam asked.

"Well, I could be careful that my clothing wasn't loose and wouldn't get caught in the belt … and I noticed the Safety Department has new mesh vests that would be cooler than this one. This vest I'm wearing is an older one, good only to stop the wind in winter."

"Getting one of the cooler vests would be a great idea!" Sam agreed. "Then you wouldn't have to worry about not being able to take care of that wonderful family of yours. Can I get your agreement you will use the cooler vest in warm weather and make certain it is zipped before you are working around the moving conveyor?" Sam reached out to shake the man's hand.

"Okay!" the man replied while shaking Sam's hand. "No problem … and gracias! Muchas gracias!"

Sam smiled, "Hey, I know you're busy, so I'll let you get back to work, but I really appreciate your talking with me."

"Thank you. I'm going find one of those new vests now," the belt man said as he walked away. "It's getting hotter."

That night at dinner, Guillermo told Sam, "I wasn't sure what was going on when you first started talking with the belt man. Then I wasn't sure the man was going to like a 'gringo' telling him how to work safely … you know our culture is different down here."

Sam smiled at that last comment. "I'm not so sure I agree, but let me explain what was happening this afternoon. One of the most important aspects of a strong safety culture is feedback," he began. "I saw the guy shoveling spillage onto a conveyor. His loose clothing could easily have caught on the roller and pulled him into the belt."

"Yes, but a lot of people aren't too happy when someone tells them they're not doing something the right way. Many of them have been working at El Cobre Gigante for years," Guillermo interrupted.

Sam nodded. "We're all like that – it's hard for us to accept feedback, but specific feedback provided in a positive way is effective across all cultures. Let me take you through a **HABIT™ Conversation**."

> *Observe*
>
> *Accentuate*
>
> *Explore*
>
> *Emphasize*
>
> *Agree*

**Step 1: Observe** means training ourselves to be more aware of a person's behaviors ... what he is doing safely and what he's doing that might put him, or someone else, at risk.

**Step 2: Accentuate** the positive to lower a person's natural defensiveness, as well as reinforce those safe behaviors we want him to keep doing.

**Step 3: Explore** allows a person to figure out what he did safely or at-risk, which helps him begin to take 'ownership' of his behavior.

**Step 4: Reinforce** the consequences of a person's actions to help him understand the impact an incident could have on him, as well as other people.

**Step 5: Agree** on future actions confirms a person understands he is accountable for his behaviors and responsible for his safety, as well as the safety of those around him.

"You've given me a lot to think about," Guillermo responded, "but let me ask you this, why do you call it a *HABIT*™ *Conversation?*"

"Well … it is actually something Kurt came up with to remind people to *Make Safety a HABIT*™ and it stands for:

*H*alt

*A*t-risk

*B*ehavior

*I*mpacting

*T*ask™

"That's great!" Guillermo exclaimed. "But let me just say this: When I saw you talking to the belt man this afternoon, I wondered if you realized we're different down here. Our culture is different, our lives are different … but after seeing how you handled that situation and hearing what you've shared with me tonight, I'm learning we're not as different as I thought."

Sam shook his hand. "My hope is everyone will start thinking about safe behaviors in everything they do, both on and off the job," Sam said.

Guillermo was thoughtful for a moment. "If everyone could have *HABIT*™ *Conversations* like the one I observed this afternoon, it would help us all get home safely to our families, which is something everyone wants to do."

# MINER'S LAMP

## DEFINITIONS:

1. ***HABIT*™ *Conversation*:** specific feedback provided in a positive way to encourage someone to demonstrate safe behaviors.

2. ***H*alt**
   ***A*t-risk**
   ***B*ehavior**
   ***I*mpacting**
   ***T*ask**™

## ESSENTIAL CONCEPTS:

✦ Risk is determined by the probability of an incident occurring given the associated hazards.

✦ Risk assessing is consciously and purposefully deciding how we are not going to get hurt.
   1. What am I doing?
   2. What might be hazardous about what I'm doing?
   3. What can I do to reduce those hazards?

✦ Since everything we do carries an element of risk and our survival depends on how well we manage those risks, even seemingly simple tasks such as driving or how we sit at our desks should be risk assessed.

✦ The more hazards we can eliminate, the lower the risk.

✦ The five steps of a *HABIT*™ *Conversation* are:

**Step 1: *Observe*** means training ourselves to be more aware of a person's behaviors ... what he is doing safely and what he's doing that might put him, or someone else, at risk.

**Step 2:** *Accentuate* the positive to lower a person's natural defensiveness as well as reinforce those safe behaviors we want him to keep doing.

**Step 3:** *Explore* allows a person to figure out what he did safely or at-risk, which helps him begin to take 'ownership' of his behavior.

**Step 4:** *Reinforce* the consequences of a person's actions to help him understand the impact an incident could have on him, as well as other people.

**Step 5:** *Agree* on future actions confirms a person understands he is accountable for his behaviors, and responsible for his safety, as well as the safety of those around him.

# MANAGEMENT'S BUY-IN — THE FOUNDATION OF EVERY SAFETY CULTURE

Kurt was eager to meet with his boss after the trip to Chile and made sure Sam could attend the meeting as well. "I'm new at this," he told Sam, "so I want you to make sure I dot all the i's and cross all the t's."

Ron Kaiser greeted the two men in his office. "I've been looking forward to this meeting," he said. "As I've mentioned before, Bradshaw, these recurring incidents are costing us time as well as money ... so, tell me about El Cobre Gigante."

Kurt and Sam briefed the manager on what they had seen, their meetings with the employees and their conversations with some of the managers.

As they concluded, Kurt changed the focus. "Let's talk about what we need to do to build a culture of safety for the company."

"Okay ... shoot," Ron invited.

"Well, over the last few months I've been seeing things differently," Kurt admitted. "What I've learned is policies, procedures and good equipment alone don't make a strong safety culture."

"I agree," Kaiser said. "We haven't gotten the results we wanted, and our claims continue to rise."

Kurt nodded. "I've shared some of our numbers with Sam and I think we've come up with a strategy that may turn those statistics around. If we want change to occur, we need to focus on people's behavior and consciously think about what we reward and tolerate."

Kaiser looked interested. "Let's get started on this safety culture thing," he said, resting his elbows on the desk. "People have to realize safety is a priority around here."

Sam leaned forward. "If I can jump in … safety as a priority is what you want to avoid when you're building a culture of safety."

Kaiser looked confused. "What? Putting safety as a priority lets people know it's important to us."

"Have you told people in the past safety is a priority?" came Sam's quick reply.

The manager settled back in his chair, folding his arms across his chest. "Well … yes …," he admitted.

Kurt was next to speak. "In a culture of safety, safety becomes a core value in the company. It's not just a priority."

Kaiser raised an eyebrow. "So, what's the difference? Aren't you just playing with words?"

"*Priorities change. Core values remain constant,*" Sam pointed out. "If safety is only one of several priorities, it usually takes a back seat to cost cutting, operational performance or client demands.

"For example, when money becomes tight or tonnage rates fall, the focus becomes getting the job done, no matter what risks or shortcuts you have to take. When safety is a core value, the only time it becomes 'the priority' is when it comes into conflict with anything else, meaning the company commits to putting human life above all other demands."

Sam's comments had obviously caught Kaiser off guard.

"Well … uh … now that you bring it up, we do have a lot of competing demands," the executive said thoughtfully.

"What we want to do is instill safety as a value … a personal and moral one … within everyone who works for the company," Kurt explained. "Safety isn't a policy people read, remember for a few days, and then forget. Safety is something people practice at work and in their personal lives. Essentially, *every person is responsible for his or her own safety, as well as the safety of the people around them.*"

"Last year we spent over $85 million in claims due to injuries and deaths on the job," Kaiser said, leaning forward and picking up a pencil. "If your so-called behavior-based safety culture can reduce that cost, I'll be the first in line to raise safety from a priority to a core value."

Sam could sense they now had Kaiser's attention. "If the company truly embraces a behavior-based safety approach across the board, you will see a significant decline in claims related to incidents and injury.

"Using last year's figure, suppose there was only a 10 percent reduction in claims. That's $8.5 million directly to the company's bottom line.

How much rock do we have to break to generate that kind of profit? More importantly, you'll establish a culture that saves human lives ... and you can't put a price tag on that."

"Plus, think of the experience we lose when a good employee is out, even for a short period of time and when you have to put a new employee on a crew, the entire dynamic of that crew changes because these people develop such a tight-knit working relationship. So, we have to factor that into the equation and how it affects people and their production.

"If we create the type of culture that motivates people to work safely, we don't risk the unknowns of personnel changes ... but more importantly, I also think we'll lower turnover," Kurt added.

"How could a safety culture make a difference in employee turnover?" Kaiser wanted to know.

"First of all, in a strong safety culture, the company rewards safe behavior," Sam responded. "When managers 'catch employees doing something right,' they praise those employees, making them feel valued.

"Also, when a company elevates safety to a core value, promotions go to those who practice safe behaviors. That demonstrates to all employees that getting the job done safely is more important than getting the job done fast. Having safety as a core value reduces turnover because people want to work for a company that genuinely cares about the safety of its people.

"Here's another point to consider as an upside of reducing turnover," Sam added. "There are some miners who believe only 1 out of 10 people you bring on board actually 'fit' into the operation and become good employees. Like I said, having safety as a core value reduces turnover because people want an employer that genuinely cares about their safety," he concluded.

"Makes sense, and maybe the press will leave us alone and people will want to start working in this industry again," Kaiser commented. "But are we going to see management praising employees for safe behaviors all the time?"

Sam chuckled. "That would be a giant step in keeping employees – and particularly our miners – safe."

Now, it was Kurt's turn to speak. "In the type of safety culture we need to build, everyone would have the right and responsibility to stop a job if they even suspected there's something unsafe about it."

"Whoa … just a minute," Kaiser interrupted. "You mean anybody can stop the belt line at any time just because he or she doesn't think it's safe to continue?"

"Absolutely right," Sam said. "Remember what we said … they not only have the right to stop a job if they suspect something is unsafe, they have the *responsibility* to stop the job."

Kaiser shook his head. "I'm not sure I can buy that."

"In a strong safety culture, it's almost a condition of employment that you stop a job if you think there is anything that puts you or someone else at risk," Sam pointed out. "That could mean stopping the job because you don't understand what's going on.

"When you think about it, peoples' behavior is the root cause for over 95 percent of all incidents," Sam continued. "Let's go back. If safety is a core value – and that means it connects here," he said tapping his chest, "then safety comes first … period."

"Okay. Okay. I'll have to think about that, but let's talk more about stopping a job ... I need to understand this better."

"What we're saying is that anyone can call a timeout," Kurt emphasized. "If it turns out there's no problem, then that's okay. The person calling the timeout won't get in trouble."

Kaiser looked incredulous. "Say that again."

"If someone stops a job because something looks or feels unsafe or even if he just doesn't understand what is being done, there's no retaliation. They get no grief from their peers or from management. Instead, they get praised for demonstrating the behavior we want ... even if it turned out to be a false alarm."

"Man, that's a huge change." Kaiser's voice was thoughtful as he spoke. "You do realize this is gonna slow down operations if I have to trust any worker who wants to stop a job?"

Now it was Sam's turn. "Consider how much it slows down operations when there is an incident or someone gets hurt."

It was obvious Ron Kaiser was giving serious thought to what Kurt was proposing. "So, let's say we do this. We elevate safety from a priority to a core value. Then, we give people the right and responsibility to stop a job if they see ... or even think something is unsafe. Nobody jumps on their case if they're wrong. Just the opposite, they are praised for stopping the job and trying to keep the team safe. Right so far?"

"You're right on," Kurt assured.

"Okay, good. So let me go on. What happens if ... check that ... *when* a manager doesn't support this new culture?"

Kurt's voice remained confident. "If a manager doesn't support the safety of his personnel, or he doesn't trust someone to stop a job to keep everyone safe, is he the person you want on the team?

"Any manager – even the most senior or productive person on the management staff – who tolerates at-risk behaviors will eventually either change his or her perspective or the new culture will squeeze them out.

"You see," Kurt continued, "if the executive team is pushing down from the top, and the people at the sharp end of the pick are pushing up from below, there is nowhere for those supervisors to hide."

Kaiser's expression was one of shock. "We've got some supervisors who do a real good job for us … and have done so for a lot of years," he countered.

"They aren't doing a good job if they're turning a blind eye to at-risk behavior and rewarding shortcuts," Kurt said. "All that supervisor cares about is how much tonnage he moves. Ron, you know as well as I, those shortcuts are exactly the behaviors that get people hurt."

The manager was reluctant to agree. "That's a pretty tall order you're throwing out."

Sam maintained a poker face. "Or, the company can keep doing what it has already been doing with regard to safety. But to expect different results is my definition of insanity."

Sam moved to the front of his chair. "Do you have time for a story?"

Kaiser looked relieved at this chance to think about everything he had heard that afternoon. "Sure … shoot."

"About 10 years ago, I was working at an open pit copper mine. We had just celebrated more than 300 days without an incident.

"One of the mine's mechanics – Burt – was one of those people who worked harder and smarter than almost anybody at the site ... and when Burt was through with his work, he was always there to lend a hand to someone else if they needed it. Everybody liked Burt.

"It was around 4 a.m. when a big shovel we used to move the overburden went down because one of the teeth broke," Sam paused for a moment before continuing. "Those teeth were heavy, but Burt was a big strong guy who lifted weights and he had no trouble removing the broken tooth and replacing it with a new one.

"Because it was just his nature, Burt then offered to put the broken tooth in his little red one-ton pickup to get it out of the way before heading home ... and let me tell you, Burt loved being home with his wife and two daughters even more than he liked mining.

"Three or four 240-ton haul trucks sat idling while the shovel was being repaired ... and the driver of the truck closest to the shovel apparently fell asleep.

"The driver was jolted awake by the shovel operator's radio call to resume operations. On this particular morning, the shovel operator didn't check to make sure the dig area was clear before starting the cycle. Then, without honking his horn and pausing a few seconds – like he was supposed to – the haul truck driver immediately began backing up to get the next load.

"We don't know exactly why, but Burt had parked his pickup right behind that lead truck. When the driver started backing, the truck's massive tires rolled over and crushed the red pickup."

Sam stopped again, brushing something from his eyes. "I was the one who had to go tell Burt's wife and children what had happened."

Kaiser was silent as he looked at the photographs of his wife and two sons featured prominently on his wall. "I see what you mean," he murmured.

Kurt gave Ron a few moments to think before continuing. "While we were in Chile, Sam had a *HABIT*™ *Conversation* with a guy working on the belt line. The man was wearing a safety vest he had unzipped, and each time he shoveled, that vest was dangling dangerously close to the roller.

"After Sam spoke with him, that guy was not only willing to change the kind of vest he was wearing and to keep it zipped while he was working near the belt line, I think he would even speak up if he saw someone else doing something at risk. To get the results we want, employees need to understand ***feedback is the breakfast of champions***, even if it means having a difficult conversation," Kurt concluded.

"That kind of training will take time," came Kaiser's response after a moment, "and what will it cost?"

"You're right," Kurt said, "and the sooner we start, the sooner we'll be able to realize those savings we discussed earlier, which will more than cover the cost of training. But we're going to need management's commitment and unconditional support every step of the way."

"What specifically would management need to commit to?" Kaiser questioned.

"Glad you asked," Kurt grinned and showed his boss a list he had prepared before the meeting. "Here's what we need to instill a strong 'SAFETY' culture in the day-to-day operations of the company."

**S**tructure supports safety as a core value by committing to put human life ahead of all other demands.

**A**ccountability gives all employees the right/responsibility to call a timeout and rewards them for doing it, even if it's a false alarm.

**F**ollow up by demonstrating and communicating a personal commitment to safety in all of your actions.

**E**liminate people, even top producers, who tolerate at-risk behaviors.

**T**rain our people to observe at-risk behaviors and have *HABIT*™ *Conversations.*

**Y**ou are the key to an incident-free environment.

It was obvious. Ron Kaiser was not only impressed with Kurt's approach, but he was also beginning to see the possibilities. "You know, Bradshaw, I've been around for a long time and I've seen a lot of safety programs come and go. Every one of them failed to keep our people safe. But, this program of yours …."

"It's not a program," Kurt corrected. "A program has a distinct starting and stopping point. If you want to move toward an incident-free environment, you have to *Make Safety a HABIT*™ by continually reinforcing it and making sure it stays relevant as the company evolves over time."

Kaiser cleared his throat. "It's apparent I'm going to have to change my thinking – and my vocabulary – about this whole safety issue," he said, in a strange way apologizing for his lack of insight. "But, I'm confident this is something we can – and will – do."

Kurt was pleased with his boss's response. "I agree."

Kaiser smiled for the first time since the meeting had begun. "I'm willing to help our people move safety from their heads to their hearts," he said. "The future of our company belongs to those who have the courage to call a timeout, the ability to speak up and the willingness to listen."

Sam looked at Kurt. "I think Ron is ready to make this journey with us."

# MINER'S LAMP

## ESSENTIAL CONCEPTS:

+ In a strong safety culture, safety is elevated to be a core value in the company. It's not just a priority. (Priorities change. Core values remain constant.)

+ Having safety as a core value reduces turnover and attracts new people because everyone wants to work for a company that genuinely cares about their safety.

+ Policies, procedures and equipment alone don't make a strong safety culture.

+ All people are responsible for their own safety, as well as the safety of the people around them.

+ To change a culture, focus on peoples' behaviors, consciously rewarding safe behaviors and not tolerating at-risk behaviors.

+ In a culture of safety, each of us has the right and responsibility to stop a job if we even suspect there's something unsafe about it.

+ Everyone – even the most senior manager or high producer – who tolerates at-risk behaviors will eventually either change their perspective or the new safety culture will squeeze them out.

+ In a strong safety culture, we understand feedback is the breakfast of champions, even if it means having a difficult conversation.

**Remember:**

✦ To demonstrate management buy-in to a culture of safety, 24/7:

**S**tructure supports safety as a core value by committing to put human life ahead of all other demands.

**A**ccountability gives all employees the right/responsibility to call a timeout and rewards them for doing it, even if it's a false alarm.

**F**ollow up by demonstrating and communicating a personal commitment to safety in all of your actions.

**E**liminate people, even top producers, who tolerate at-risk behaviors.

**T**rain our people to observe at-risk behaviors and have *HABIT*™ *Conversations*.

**Y**ou are the key to an incident-free environment.

# GIVING AND RECEIVING FEEDBACK

After his meeting with Ron Kaiser, Kurt was ready to begin implementing the new safety culture. Realistically, he didn't expect changes to occur overnight; he knew it would be built one step at a time.

"I'm going to unveil the concept at the supervisors' meeting today," he told Jessica over breakfast that morning. "I am going to stress to them the importance of giving and receiving feedback."

"Communicating has always been one of your strengths," his wife responded. "You recognize **listening is more than just waiting for your turn to talk.**"

Kurt hugged his wife before heading for the door. "Wish me luck today."

✦ ✦ ✦ ✦ ✦

Kurt felt good about his agenda for the meeting. After a few icebreakers, Kurt was ready to introduce some of the key components for the new safety culture.

"It's called a Safety Culture for several reasons," he began. "First, the word 'culture' describes the beliefs and behaviors of a group of people that are transmitted from one generation to another.

"In a company, that means what experienced personnel pass along to new hires. With our international operations, the term 'culture' also refers to the many countries represented by our work force.

"Secondly, when we are truly committed to safety, we demonstrate safe behaviors in all aspects of our lives, 24/7. Safety isn't something we 'turn on and off' at work."

Several heads nodded in agreement.

"An important concept I've learned," Kurt continued, "is in a culture of safety, feedback is the tool our teammates have for reminding us when our behaviors impact safety.

"Think about a person who gave you good feedback – feedback that motivated you or helped you see a situation for what it really was. What made that particular feedback so effective?"

"I accepted feedback better if someone described 'what' they saw me doing," said one supervisor after a few moments. "But, I didn't like it when they tried to tell me 'why' I had done it that way: For example, if they said I was just being lazy or had a bad attitude."

"Exactly. Effective feedback focuses on actions that can be observed, not attitudes … because we can never really know what someone else is thinking," said Kurt. "Good point! Someone else?"

A foreman sitting at the far table smiled. "Many years ago, a coach sat me down and talked to me straight. He was very direct and specific on what I needed to do. I could tell he truly believed what he told me. I'll never forget him or what he did for my life."

"The feedback I remember was from my sergeant in the Army," came the reply from another supervisor. "He could have made me feel like the lowest person in the world. Don't get me wrong, he was in my face, but he also praised some of my good qualities and said he believed in me."

"These are all great examples and show you already know effective feedback is based upon a sincere desire to help someone improve. Plus, it focuses on what the person is doing right as well as what he could do better."

"Okay, I've got a question for you," one of the older mine supervisors said. "From a safety standpoint, I've often seen people do something risky because they think, 'I can get away with it.' What's the best way to handle that?"

Kurt immediately thought of his first meeting with Sam. "We have a name for those behaviors," he said. "We call them 'old school' or 'bullet-proof' because the person doesn't think they, or anyone else, will ever get hurt by their actions. But let me ask you something. What did you do when you saw someone take that risk?"

"Well, they got the job done, so I didn't say anything," came the reply.

"You're not alone in handling the situation like that. We've all done it – but what we're doing when we ignore these behaviors is actually rewarding and encouraging the employee to take risks in the future," Kurt pointed out. "People are essentially practicing for their next incident.

"In a culture of safety, we need to provide that person with our feedback to help him change his behaviors."

"But isn't the other person's behavior out of our control?" asked a new supervisor from the crusher.

Kurt was thoughtful before he responded. "Yes, ultimately a person is responsible for his own behavior, but what I have to ask myself is 'have I provided him feedback in a manner that motivates him to change his behavior?' If not, then I am accountable if an incident does take place, which is why providing effective feedback is so important."

✦ ✦ ✦ ✦ ✦

Kurt started the second part of the meeting by writing, '**_Trust is essential in a culture of safety_**,' on the board and asking the question, "How many of you trust everyone you work with?"

He waited a moment or two. Not a single hand went up. "Okay, let me ask another question. What does it mean when you trust somebody?"

"To me, it means having confidence in that person," said a heavy-equipment supervisor who came from generations of miners. "I think I learned that from my grandfather."

"It means they've delivered on what they promised in the past," said another supervisor.

"Your answers are right on," Kurt responded. "Trusting someone means believing in them and what they say. It's knowing that person is sincere."

"My wife trusts everyone. For me, people have to earn my trust," a mill maintenance supervisor spoke up.

"Good point," Kurt said. "Whether or not you immediately trust someone, a key step in building a culture of safety is to 'commit' to building trust. Do you risk being deceived or disappointed? Absolutely. There are risks involved in making this commitment because, as we all know, sometimes trusting a person backfires – and the results leave us feeling ripped off or embarrassed. However, if we don't start trusting each other, the long-term consequences are much worse.

"So, in order to build our safety culture, I'm asking you to make a sincere commitment to trust the person providing you the feedback … and here's what you've got to do to fulfill the commitment," he said, turning toward something he had written on a large piece of paper and stuck on the wall:

Building trust requires your willingness to:

- ✦ Recognize the person may see things differently than you do (and you can still both be right)
- ✦ Be receptive (you may not know everything)
- ✦ Listen (not say, 'I know')
- ✦ Ask questions
- ✦ Focus on areas of agreement
- ✦ Act on the feedback
- ✦ Follow up

Kurt gave the group a chance to absorb the information.

***"In a culture of safety, trust throughout the company is critical,"*** Kurt said. "Let me ask, has anyone been to a marine park that has a show using killer whales?"

A few of the men slowly raised their hands.

"Bet you're wondering what killer whales have to do with feedback and trust," Kurt chuckled. "Considered one of the most feared predators in the ocean, killer whales weigh several tons and can kill just about anything. *Whale Done!* a book by Ken Blanchard, tells about the trainers at Sea World who not only get into the tanks with these giants but also ride on their backs.

"Blanchard's book details how the trainers motivate whales to perform, and the first thing Blanchard talks about is trust – not just trainers trusting the whales but the whales trusting the trainers.

"How many of you would want to get in the tank with a killer whale that had just been punished for not doing what it was supposed to do? I know I don't respond very positively when people yell at me."

"Me neither," said one of the electrical supervisors, sitting at the back of the room. "Never have, never will."

"When a whale does what the trainer wants, it is praised and rewarded. If the whale gets off track, the trainer sets up another objective – maybe a repeat of the last one – so the whale can be successful and get rewarded," Kurt explained. "So how can we apply this to our own people?"

"I guess what you are saying is if someone does something at-risk, it's not a good idea to ignore it or yell at them. Instead, we need to redirect them in order for them to be successful," one of the supervisors volunteered.

"Exactly," Kurt affirmed. "And why is it not a good idea to simply tell someone 'Don't do that again'?"

"Because there is a reason why the person did what they did, and unless we understand what motivated them to do it that way, we shouldn't expect them to change their behavior just because we want them to," one of the lead pit technicians explained with a Spanish accent.

"You guys are quickly understanding the logic behind the culture of safety we want to build here and across the company," Kurt praised.

By the end of the week, Kurt was sure he was on the right track. His meetings had gone as well as he had expected and Kurt believed he had earned buy-in from several on his team.

"They've been willing to listen, once we discussed the impact our safety statistics have on their operations," Kurt said as he helped Jessica put away the dinner dishes. "I will admit, my expectations have been pretty high, but so far I haven't been disappointed."

"You've always operated with a positive attitude and high expectations," his wife replied supportively. "Remember how we were the summer before Shannon went into middle school? We thought she'd shut us out of her life and we wouldn't know any of her friends."

"Oh, man, I lost lots of sleep during that period in her life," Kurt remembered.

"But, we trusted Shannon and believed she would make good decisions," Jessica continued. "By having those expectations and rewarding the good choices she made, Shannon never let us down."

"Well, with all her studying and sports, she didn't really have time … and after all, she is her daddy's girl," Kurt chuckled.

"You're right," Jessica agreed, "but trust, along with high expectations, can make a big difference."

✦  ✦  ✦  ✦  ✦

When Kurt arrived at Sam's the following day, he was surprised to see two other men. "Kurt, I wanted you to get to know these guys," Sam began the introductions.

"I've told them about your task and what you've been doing over the last 60 days. Both are experienced hard-rock miners, and since you mentioned you wanted to talk about feedback, I thought it would be good to hear their comments. Meet Cy Thomas and Mark Wilson."

The two men stood and shook Kurt's hand. Both appeared to be in their late 60s, had weathered faces and calloused hands, so Kurt knew they'd spent a lot of time in the pit.

Kurt briefed the trio on the high points of his meetings during the past week. "Some of the supervisors voiced concerns about their people wanting to provide feedback to co-workers," he said.

Mark Wilson was the first to speak up. His voice was gruff but his eyes were wise. "I can see their point. It's tough to offer feedback to people, especially co-workers who have been on the job longer than you. However, if you can help people understand you genuinely care about their safety, they're usually more willing to listen.

"But, giving feedback is only half of it. People also need to learn how to receive feedback effectively. Sam told me what we were gonna talk about so I wrote down a few things that have helped me over the years. At my age, if I don't write it down, I don't remember it, so here goes:

> ✦ *I sincerely listen to the feedback people offer.*
> ✦ *I separate what the person says from what I think about the person.*
> ✦ *I don't over-react to feedback.*

✦ *If I'm not clear about what they're saying, I ask open, non-defensive questions.*

✦ *Even when I disagree with parts of the feedback, I focus on areas where I can improve.*

Kurt reviewed the list. "Those are all great points," he said.

Cy Thomas was a slight, wiry man who spoke with a Canadian accent and was dressed in overalls. "The important point for people to remember is that the consequence of not offering feedback can be devastating. Feedback can literally be the difference between life and death."

"So, is it harder to give feedback than to receive it?" Kurt wanted to know.

"Depends on your attitude. Think about the last time your wife gave you feedback. How would you respond, if let's say you were climbing a ladder to fix something up high and your wife came out and made a suggestion – like waiting for a professional to fix a problem."

Kurt thought for a moment before responding, "If I was in a hurry, I might say something like, 'If you don't think I can do this job to your liking, why don't you just say so?'"

The others laughed. "Me, too," Cy admitted. "But, if I believed my wife genuinely cared about me, I would realize she was saying it for my own well-being, and I would be more likely to follow her advice," Cy said, looking away to avoid Sam's steely gaze.

"It also depends on the other person's history of providing you feedback," Mark pointed out. "If your wife was what I call a 'seagull,' only swooping in to dump negative feedback on you all the time, maybe you wouldn't listen as closely or do what she suggested."

"The same is true with miners … or any employees for that matter," Cy said. "If you're on their backs constantly, how open do you think they'll be to your feedback, even if it could impact their safety? It's important for people to get feedback on an ongoing basis, but the majority of it should be about things they're doing right … and telling someone 'I told you so' can never be considered positive feedback.

"Remember, it's not just supervisors who give feedback. Everyone does. In fact, co-workers are more likely to be around when opportunities for feedback come up, since there are more of them. It just takes courage to speak up. That's why building trust is the first step," Cy concluded.

"Let me add one thing here," Sam paused and took a deep breath. "I've been in situations where honest feedback was given, someone chose to ignore it and a serious injury happened. Once feedback is given, there's always the question: Will the person choose to change his behavior?"

The room was silent. Finally Kurt spoke, "Like you said in our first meeting, Sam. We need to help our people take that information from here," pointing to his head, "and move it to here," he added as he tapped his heart.

Sam smiled. He knew Kurt had learned this lesson well.

 # MINER'S LAMP

## ESSENTIAL CONCEPTS:

✦ Feedback is the tool our teammates have for reminding us when our at-risk behaviors impact safety.

✦ Effective feedback is based upon a sincere desire to help someone improve and focuses on:

1. Actions that can be observed, not *attitudes* – because we can never really know what someone else is thinking.

2. What the person is doing right as well as what he could do better.

✦ Ultimately, everyone is responsible for their own behavior, but we still need to ask ourselves, "Have I provided him feedback in a manner that motivates him to change his behaviors?" If not, then we are accountable if an incident takes place.

✦ When building a culture of safety, if you can help people understand you genuinely care about their safety, they're usually more willing to listen to feedback.

✦ Trust is essential in a culture of safety.

✦ We shouldn't expect peoples' behaviors to change just because we want them to.

✦ We can learn how to receive feedback effectively by:

• *Sincerely listening to the feedback people offer (listening is more than just waiting for your turn to talk).*

• *Separating what the person says from what I think about the person.*

• *Never overreacting to feedback.*

&#10070; *Asking open, non-defensive questions if I'm not clear about what they're saying.*

&#10070; *Focusing on areas where I can improve, even when I disagree with feedback.*

&#10022; The consequences of not offering feedback can be devastating … it can literally be the difference between life and death.

&#10022; It's important for people to receive feedback on an ongoing basis, but the majority of it should be about things they're doing right.

&#10022; Once feedback is given, there's always the question: Will the person choose to change his behavior?

# 8 Maintaining Momentum

Back in his office after a whirlwind schedule of training sessions at various mine sites around the country and overseas, Kurt was cautiously optimistic about his goal of creating a culture of safety for his company.

In the past, safety had been a priority until something more urgent came up. It was becoming clear. Building a strong safety culture required everyone in the company – from the president to the newest hire – to understand the importance of making safety a core value, not just a priority that changes as needs arise.

At the various job sites he visited, Kurt emphasized this: "It's not a new initiative. The whole emphasis is on taking the good things we are already doing and ingraining them in our culture so everyone 'walks the talk' every day, in every area of our operations, and every part of their lives, 24/7."

Kurt remembered a comment from a shovel operator who had been around for many years: "You can talk to me about safety all you want. Just don't tell me how to do my job."

"Talk about old school mentality," Kurt mumbled as he switched on his computer. "That attitude will keep people from speaking about their concerns. *You can't be open to safety feedback if you aren't open to all feedback.*"

Thinking more about that supervisor, Kurt began typing an e-mail to the supervisors he had met during his training sessions. He titled it: "*Maintaining an Incident-Free Culture.*"

> "During the last 90 days, many of you have helped me learn what it takes to build a strong safety culture. You've helped me realize in order to build the culture we want, **we must consciously think about what our actions demonstrate, reward and tolerate**.
>
> "It's not easy and it's not something that happens by itself because our normal actions usually reinforce old habits, which only help to maintain the current culture. Here's an example:
>
> "Consider the mine worker who takes a shortcut to get a job done. If the supervisor rewards the end result without realizing the shortcut involved at-risk behaviors, the supervisor has, unconsciously, rewarded those behaviors … and that miner may just use those behaviors again and again … or until he gets hurt.
>
> "As supervisors, we also need to consider what we tolerate in our employees. Is it possible we overlook certain at-risk behaviors because it is easier to ignore them than to deal with them?

"Do we make excuses for our employees – and for ourselves –
by saying, 'Oh, that's just how Jaime does things,' or, 'I don't
have time to deal with it now. Besides, Human Resources
never does anything, even if I write up an employee who's
put himself – or others – at risk?'"

"I want you to think about these points and then answer the
following questions:

✦ What do your actions say to other people? Do you
    continually demonstrate safety is a core value to you?

✦ What behaviors do you reward in other people? Do
    you only look at the outcome of a job and not the
    risks taken to get it done quickly?

✦ What behaviors do you tolerate? Do you find
    excuses not to speak up?

Kurt ended his e-mail by reinforcing the need for praise in a changing
culture. He also included suggestions about how to praise performance
from Ken Blanchard's book, *Whale Done* – called "The Whale Done
Response:"

✦ Praise people immediately

✦ Be specific about what they did right ... or almost right

✦ Share your positive feelings

✦ Encourage them to keep up the good work

The following morning, responses began to come in.

One supervisor wrote:

"There are several employees who think this whole thing
is just another weak attempt to try and polish the
company's safety record, and they don't think it's worth

making any real changes because they believe it will go away, just like past safety initiatives have. At any rate, they're giving me fits and may never get to the place where they take it seriously. I feel like a failure ... any ideas?"

"Yeah," said Kurt to himself. "I've seen that resistance at every job site I've visited and it isn't pretty."

He e-mailed the supervisor this response:

"Cultural change is never easy. You are asking people to change the way they've been doing things for years. The old culture will fight it at every opportunity.

"When trying to change a culture, it is natural for us to spend time with the small number of people who resist change. That's NOT where we want to spend our energy. Those 'resistors' are not going to change quickly.

"Instead, team up with the 'supporters' of change. This helps in two ways: First, the supporters are the champions you need to keep onboard. They have a tough role and can easily get discouraged because they're the ones on the front lines, taking all the flak. They need your frequent – and visible – support to know they've made the right decision. Plus, hearing you reward the supporters will help others get off the fence and align with the supporters. Getting the 'fence-sitters' onboard – combined with your tough love – will provide the momentum necessary to change the resistors."

But, out of all the e-mails Kurt received, the one that moved him most was the one that had been written from the heart:

I could have saved a life that day,
But I chose to look the other way.
It wasn't that I didn't care,
I had the time, and I was there.
But I didn't want to seem a fool,
Or argue over a safety rule.

I knew he'd done the job before,
If I called it wrong, he might get sore.
The chances didn't seem that bad,
I have done the same, he knew I had.
So I shook my head and walked on by,
He knew the risk as well as I.
He took the chance, I closed an eye,
And with that act, I let him die.

I could have saved a life that day,
But I chose to look the other way.
Now every time I see his wife,
I'll know I should have saved his life.
That guilt is something I must bear,
But it isn't something you need share.
If you see a risk that others take,
That puts their health or life at stake.
The question asked, or thing you say,
Could help him live another day.

If you see a risk and walk away,
Then hope you never have to say,
I could have saved a life that day,
But I chose to look the other way.

✦ ✦ ✦ ✦ ✦

Later that afternoon Kurt picked up his daughter, Shannon, from softball practice. "How was it today?" Kurt asked as she fastened her seat belt.

"It was pretty cool," was the teenager's enthusiastic reply.

Since her team had been struggling recently and the coach was initiating several changes on the field, Shannon's response was a welcomed surprise for Kurt. "Yeah, how come?" he asked.

"Well, Coach started the practice by reminding everyone of our goal to win the division championship. Then he talked about why he had made some specific changes and said no matter how strong a team is, he knows each of us will react differently when changes are introduced," Shannon said, taking a piece of paper out of her workout bag.

"Coach said change typically causes people to have concerns like:
+ *How will the change impact me personally?*
+ *What's in it for me?*
+ *Will I win or lose?*
+ *Will I look good?*
+ *Will I have enough time to learn my new position?*
+ *Can I do it?*
+ *What if I don't like it?*

"Those are all good questions," Kurt agreed. "So then what happened?"

"Well, first it just made me feel better, knowing my worries were normal. I was beginning to wonder if I would even be playing.

Then Coach sat down with each of us and talked about our individual strengths. He helped me see how my past experience and success could help me in the future … and he gave me some new stuff to think about, too. Now I understand why he made the changes and, more importantly, how those changes will affect me. So now I can concentrate on my new role on the team," Shannon concluded with a smile.

"Your coach sounds like he really knows how to lead people. Mind if I borrow that list?" Kurt asked, thinking of the team he was trying to build.

The following day, Kurt went by Sam's house to bring him up to date on what he'd been doing. "Sam, I think everything is going pretty much the way I envisioned, thanks in no small part to you," he said. "I also think a majority of our employees are excited about building a strong safety culture. Now, one of my main concerns is how to keep the momentum going."

Sam smiled. "You've just been through the birth and delivery of your culture of safety. Now you want to make sure it has the opportunity to grow?"

"That's a pretty good analogy," Kurt agreed.

"I want to share something I read several years ago about maintaining momentum." Sam pulled a folded piece of paper from his pocket, smoothing it so Kurt could read the words:

When changing a culture:

- ✦ Don't expect to be popular.
- ✦ Recruit help.
- ✦ Educate and train.

✦ Champion change at every opportunity.

✦ Measure and reward results.

✦ Have the courage to stick with it.

"Hmmm ... some good ideas here," Kurt said, "but I'd like to talk about the details."

"Glad to," Sam said. "Let's begin with:

**Don't expect to be popular.**
"In any culture change, that small group of people who want to hold on to their old behaviors will use every opportunity to discredit both you and the new culture you are creating. Remember, you're doing what you sincerely believe is necessary to help the company and the people. You're not out to win a popularity contest."

Kurt shook his head. "That's pretty straight forward," he agreed.

"Moving on to:

**Recruit help.**
"Achieving a strong Safety Culture requires a team effort. It doesn't merely have to be supervisors talking with employees. When team members begin talking to other team members about safety behaviors, it doesn't matter if the supervisor is around or not. The safety culture will become self-supporting because there's almost always another team member around to have those important *HABIT* ™ *Conversations.*"

"Got it. The supervisor doesn't have to carry the entire load himself," Kurt said. "Just like I mentioned earlier, it makes so much sense when you lay out the big picture. Keep going. This is good stuff!"

**Educate and train.**

"This means educating employees about why change is necessary and then working with them to develop new behaviors. For example, the training you're doing on how to give and receive feedback," Sam said. "Until everyone knows how to do it, they'll stay in their comfort zones and stick with the old way of doing things."

**Champion the change at every opportunity.**

"Employees watch their leaders to see how committed they are to the culture change," Sam continued. "Communicate the successes. Tell stories about how people are meeting the standard. Talk about the difference in their incident numbers, and compare how they are doing now with how they were doing before the change took place."

"Sort of like a cheerleader?" Kurt asked.

"Cheerleading is certainly part of it, but so is motivating, teaching, and – since you're down in the trenches, too – leading by example. I like to think of it more as a player-coach scenario. Make safety a part of every meeting, every conversation. Any time it's possible, talk about improving your culture of safety."

"I'm ready," Kurt said.

**Measure and reward results.**

"Decide what you will measure, then communicate those measurements and make the results known immediately. Short-term reporting helps employees see you're serious about tracking the changes that are needed," Sam said.

"Many companies fail to follow up. Once employees realize you're totally committed to building a strong safety culture, more fence-sitters will be convinced to join the early adaptors."

"Okay," said Kurt.

**Have the courage to stick with it.**

"How do you think a supervisor feels after a day of beating his or her head against the wall, trying to convert resistors? Now think about how they'd feel after a day of working with the early adaptors who support the new safety culture. Remind your supervisors – it feels a lot better rewarding those early adaptors. It's less stressful catching people doing something right," Sam pointed out, "and you know from your own experience that changing a culture creates a whole new brand of stress."

Kurt nodded his agreement.

"There will always be plenty of push-back from the resistors, always a lot of people questioning what you're doing," Sam empathized. "Sometimes, you'll even question yourself about whether or not you're doing the right thing."

"Been there a lot lately," Kurt admitted.

"I'm sure you've also had times when you felt it would just be a lot easier to chuck the whole process and go back to the way things were … but don't do it. It takes courage to stand your ground and not back down for an easier journey, and you need to regularly remind yourself why you're doing this.

"Whenever the going gets tough," Sam continued, "you'll have to imagine how good it's going to feel – for you, all your people, and their families – when they *know* their loved one will come home each night."

 # MINER'S LAMP

### ESSENTIAL CONCEPTS:

+ You can't be open to safety feedback if you aren't open to all feedback.

+ To build a strong safety culture, we must consciously think about what our actions demonstrate, reward and tolerate.

+ To build a culture of safety, you are asking people to change habits. Expect the old culture to fight the culture change at every opportunity.

+ Team up with the 'supporters' of change to help the 'fence-sitters' get onboard, which will provide the momentum necessary to change the 'resistors.'

+ When making changes, people will always have individual concerns:

    ✧ How will the change impact me personally?
    ✧ What's in it for me?
    ✧ Will I win or lose?
    ✧ Will I look good?
    ✧ Will I have enough time to learn my new position?
    ✧ Can I do it?
    ✧ What if I don't like it?

+ When people can honestly say, 'I believe in safety for myself and actively encourage my teammates to believe in safety,' their passion for safety comes from their heart, not just their head.

✦ When changing a culture:

  ✧ Don't expect to be popular
  ✧ Recruit help
  ✧ Educate and train
  ✧ Champion change at every opportunity
  ✧ Measure and reward results
  ✧ Have the courage to stick with it

# 9 KEEPING IT REAL

"Two weeks to go," Kurt sighed as he glimpsed at the calendar on his desk. But, he felt good about the progress they had made over the last 3 ½ months.

"We're not starting another new program," he repeated time and again as he traveled around the world. "We want to strengthen our existing safety culture by addressing the human element."

In some cases, his approach was, predictably, met with resistance, but momentum started to grow as more people began taking responsibility for their own safety, as well as those around them and, more importantly, incident rates started coming down at the mines he had visited.

His ringing phone jolted Kurt out of his thoughts.

"Ron! Sure! I'll be right up," he said.

His boss had sounded rattled. When Kurt walked through the door, he found Ron staring at a map on the wall behind his desk.

"Glad you were in town," Kaiser began, his words coming in rapid-fire succession. "We've just had a serious incident in one of our joint-venture projects in China. We need to begin focusing our efforts there. But with the cultural differences, I'm not sure this new process will work in that part of the world. Maybe we need to try something different."

Kurt listened as Kaiser provided the details and thought about his answer before he spoke, making certain his voice remained calm but assertive. "I am confident our new culture of safety is powerful enough to transcend geographic and cultural differences because, as hard as it may be to believe, human behavior is the same wherever we go."

"What about their different beliefs, customs and traditions?" Kaiser wondered. "They don't think about things the same way we do."

Kurt was ready for Ron's questions. "What we need to focus on are those things people have in common, no matter what country they are from. Think of it this way ... if we line up five people from different cultures, including China, and I walk by and jump on each of their feet, tell me in what culture that wouldn't hurt?"

Kaiser seemed to be searching for the right answer. "Well ... uh ... of course it would hurt," he said finally.

"Exactly," Kurt countered. "A person's desire not to get injured is universal. There are other things we all have in common as well, like the bond of family, the need for food, the desire to remain employed and the need for respect.

"Here's an idea. Why don't we call John Sullivan and talk with him about what he's encountered with the multiple cultures he works with in South America?"

Kaiser agreed and hit the speed dial on his phone. "Sullivan? Ron

Kaiser. I've got Kurt Bradshaw here and we need your thoughts on our new safety culture. We've got you on speaker phone."

"I'll be happy to give you my take," John said, his Australian accent apparent in every word. "G'day, Kurt."

"Keeping out of trouble down there?" Kurt joked.

"Yea, I'm behaving myself," John retorted, "and Theresa is keeping an eagle eye on me, as well … and you'll be glad to know I haven't been behind the wheel, well, since your last visit, Mate."

Then his tone turned serious. "So, what do you want to know about safety in South America … because I know you've seen some of the positive results."

"I need to know why you think it's working," Kaiser said. "What are you seeing, especially among the different nationalities working together down there?"

After a moment, John responded. "What I'm seeing are supervisors taking time to mentor, encourage and congratulate their teams on the job they're doing. I'm seeing people walk a little taller, with more confidence and, best of all, employees are seeing co-workers take care of each other, regardless of where they're from.

"What's happened is people are actually having *HABIT*™ *Conversations* and calling timeouts. That alone seems to be driving down our incident rate. Our miners and supervisors like our new safety culture because it matches the desire every person has to go home from work in the same shape he was in when he arrived."

Kaiser still looked skeptical. "Tell me what else is different."

"Well, we've developed a group of safety champions – people who are leading the charge … and in addition to encouraging *HABIT*™ *Conversations* between all levels of staff, we've made sure to reward behaviors we value," John continued.

"Also, as you know, several weeks ago we terminated a member of our management team … a guy who always turned a blind eye to at-risk behaviors, which confirmed to everyone that nothing is more important here than their safety and the safety of their co-workers."

Kurt smiled and gave Kaiser a big thumbs up. Kaiser nodded his agreement.

John continued, "But what's been really great is our people are using *HABIT*™ **Cards** to reduce risks, regardless of what language they speak. Of course, there are still those instances where someone will take a shortcut or do something at-risk, but most of the time, there's someone in the area who stops them before an incident occurs."

"Okay," Kaiser interrupted. "So, do you think what you're doing in South America can work in China?"

"If it works here," John said, "it can work anywhere. Remember, we have a real diverse work force. Depending upon the country, we'll have multiple languages on every shift. But our people all share the need to stay healthy, get a paycheck and feed their families."

"We may need to adapt 'how' we deliver the message, or the methodology of the training," Kurt pointed out, "but what John is saying is people are people, anywhere you go, and *a person's underlying motivations for working safely are universal.*"

Kaiser looked at his watch. "Well, you guys convinced me it will work across different cultures. I'm astounded at the progress," he said. "I have 5 minutes to get to a meeting … so we have to end it here. Sullivan, you're doing a great job down there … and we're glad to have you back on the job. Bradshaw, let's get started in China."

As he prepared to leave his office that day, Kurt glanced at the photograph of his great-grandmother, standing outside the company store at Monagah. It could have easily been a reflection from the sun shining through the window … but it appeared the pale woman in the long, dark dress was actually smiling her approval at what her great-grandson had accomplished.

✦ ✦ ✦ ✦ ✦

Monday night, Kurt and Jessica invited Sam out to dinner to thank him for all of his help.

"I've heard so much about you, I feel like I already know you," Jessica said to Sam after her husband had completed the introductions.

"And I can't tell you how much I've wanted to meet Kurt's partner … and, if I heard him correctly, his better half," Sam replied. "I had hoped my wife, Edith, would be able to join us, but she was called away suddenly to take care of her mother. I hope you don't mind Kurt and me talking business for a few minutes. I'm always eager to hear what's been happening with the new safety culture."

"Everything so far has been working well with only a couple of glitches along the way. Through Ron's support, we've gained momentum and have upper management's buy-in."

Jessica jumped in. "Kurt makes it sound easy, but trust me, it sure didn't start out that way."

"How so?" Sam wanted to know.

"I'm not sure I shared with you how nervous I was about taking this job," Kurt began.

"I think your exact words were something like, 'What do I know about safety? It's entirely different than operations,'" his wife recalled.

"That's exactly what I thought," Kurt continued. "I couldn't see how being successful in operations would help me improve safety.

Over time, though, I began to realize that regardless of where I worked in the company, I needed to:

- ✦ *Build a foundation of trust.*
- ✦ *Set clear goals and high expectations.*
- ✦ *Praise progress as people begin changing behaviors.*
- ✦ *Have the courage to keep going.*

"Sounds like you now realize **the skills necessary to be a good safety leader are the same skills necessary to be a good leader**, period," Sam stated.

"If I had recognized in the beginning that **operations and safety are 'interdependent,'** I could have saved myself a lot of anxiety."

"When you were in operations, if anyone had told you **safety is as much your responsibility as it is for the people who work in the safety department**, would you have believed it?" Sam asked.

"No, probably not," Kurt admitted. "But now I realize safety supervisors are here to 'support' us, and it is not their job to keep everyone safe anymore than it is mine."

"Hey, is anybody hungry besides me?" Jessica interrupted as she picked up her menu. "If we don't order soon, they might ask us to leave."

Once the waiter had taken their orders, Kurt was ready to cut to the chase. "Sam, one of the reasons we wanted to have dinner tonight was to thank you for everything you've done to help me the past four months. I want you to know, my friend, how grateful I am for your encouragement and patience as well as your willingness to listen and provide guidance every step of the way."

Then it was Jessica's turn. "Kurt said you were one of those people who had everything, but we want to give you something to let you know how much we appreciate all you've done." She handed him a gift-wrapped box.

Inside was a set of bookends Kurt had asked a local artist to create, depicting a ladder, used in the old coal mines, and a small hardhat outfitted with a miner's lamp.

Sam studied the attractive bronze pieces. "Thank you," he said in a strangely soft voice. "You don't know the amazing irony of your gift."

Kurt set down his iced tea glass and leaned forward to hear as Sam told his story.

"Years ago, when my son Jason was just a kid, he and I were getting ready to spend the afternoon together. But, before I left, I wanted to check a problem with the roof of our house. Edith had called a professional roofer and he was scheduled to come the next week, but as both of you know, miners think they can fix anything.

"About the same time, my wife came out on the back porch to see why we hadn't left and I was just climbing the ladder. Edith asked if she could help hold the ladder and, as you might expect, I told her 'No, I can handle this myself.'

"Well, I found the problem with the roof where shingles had blown away during a storm and there was a small hole. Edith tried again to get me off the roof, but I was stubborn … so she went back into the house. On her way in, however, she asked our son, Jason, who was skateboarding, to hold the ladder for me.

But I fired back, 'He's fine. This won't take but a minute.'"

Sam paused a moment in his story. "Remember when we talked about how sometimes honest feedback is given and people choose to ignore it?"

Kurt nodded.

"Well, my bullet-proof attitude got in the way of Edith's honest feedback. Two minutes after she gave up and went inside, I learned safety happens by choice … and so do incidents."

"As I began climbing down the ladder, one of the legs sank into the wet ground." Sam took another sip of tea before continuing.

"Anyway, I fell, landing in such a way that I shattered my foot. Jason helped me get my boot off and one of my ankle bones had pierced the skin. It was the worst pain I'd ever felt, and it was terrible that Jason had to witness any of it."

Jessica covered her mouth, almost visualizing the outcome.

"I was in too big of a hurry that day … anyhow, things got pretty bad.

"Edith heard Jason's screams and came running. When she saw what had happened, she had the presence of mind to call for help.

"I was fortunate, but for a while it was anybody's guess about when or if I would walk," Sam went on. "At one point the doctors wanted to amputate my foot, but then a specialist took a look, wheeled me into surgery, and pieced the shattered bones together.

"Luckily, after a couple more surgeries followed by several months of therapy, I was able to hobble around ... after about two years, I was back to walking without crutches or even a cane. Of course, I was left with this limp, which is more of an inconvenience than anything else."

"Oh, how terrible you had to go through all that," Jessica said.

"But the physical injuries weren't as bad as the other problems I caused that day."

"You caused?" Kurt asked.

"Jason was about 10 at the time and blamed himself for his dad being hurt," Sam continued. "He developed some pretty serious emotional problems, and as a result, he ran away several times and began having trouble in school.

"Finally, we found a psychologist to work with him so he wouldn't continue to carry so much guilt," the older man explained, "but from the day of the incident and for many years afterward, Jason wasn't comfortable around me. It drove a real wedge into our relationship."

"What about Edith?" Jessica wondered.

"I really wish she could have been here tonight," Sam said. "She's an amazing lady, but after the incident, she also felt guilty ... and I wasn't very supportive, I'm afraid.

"I went through a period of deep depression during my recovery, which put a real strain on our marriage. I wasn't able to work and money became a big issue," Sam continued. "Finally, it just got to be too much and we separated for several months. I suppose it took that long for me to come to my senses and realize I wasn't as tough as I had always thought."

"It sounds like you all learned some pretty difficult lessons," Kurt said, supportively.

"One of the greatest regrets I had was the example I set for my son. In fact, by my careless I-can-do-anything attitude, I gave him 'permission' to become reckless, too.

"It took me a while to figure it all out, but the grief Edith experienced, Jason's problems and my own injuries all could have been prevented.

"It's like the what-if game ... what if I hadn't gotten on the roof that day, what if I had allowed Edith or Jason to hold the ladder or what if I hadn't been so headstrong ... so bullet-proof?

"At any rate, after seeing the damage I caused my family and in my own life, I decided to make safety my personal crusade," Sam explained. "Incidents can be prevented. That's the message I want to get across to others. It takes someone willing to speak up and it also takes the other person being willing to listen."

Kurt reached across the table and patted Sam's arm. "I never guessed how painful your lesson was or how strongly it impacted your family."

"Just remember," Sam said. "Having an injury-free workplace is an achievable goal because incidents are preventable. Safety happens by choice and so do incidents. That's why every individual makes a difference."

✦  ✦  ✦  ✦  ✦

Later that night, Kurt had difficulty getting to sleep. He couldn't stop thinking about Sam's story.

"Honest feedback was given and someone chose to ignore it," he thought, envisioning Jason seeing his father's pain, the broken bones and going through the problems that resulted. "It is a lesson I don't want anyone to have to go through."

Ten minutes later, Kurt was ready to close his eyes, but before falling asleep, he whispered a prayer of thanks – for Sam, his wisdom and his willingness to help someone who needed his guidance.

Organizational change is a long road … and he knew he was just beginning his own journey. Minutes later, Kurt was asleep.

# MINER'S LAMP

**DEFINITIONS:**

1. **Safety champions** – people who are leading the charge, encouraging *HABIT™ Conversations* between all levels of staff, and ensuring behaviors we want to see are rewarded.

**ESSENTIAL CONCEPTS:**

✦ When we build a Safety Culture, we're strengthening our existing safety culture by addressing the human element.

✦ The Safety Culture is powerful enough to transcend geographic and cultural differences because human behavior is the same, wherever we go.

✦ What we need to focus on are those things people have in common, no matter what country they are from.

✦ People like the Safety Culture because it matches the desire every miner has to go home from work in the same shape he was in when he arrived.

✦ A person's underlying motivations for working safely are universal.

✦ The skills necessary to be a good safety leader are the same skills necessary to be a good operations leader and vice versa:

✧ Build a foundation of trust.

✧ Set clear goals and high expectations.

✧ Praise progress as people begin changing behaviors.

✧ Have the courage to keep going.

✦ Operations and safety are 'interdependent.'

+ Safety is as much everyone's responsibility as it is for the people who work in the safety department.

+ Having an injury-free workplace is an achievable goal because incidents **are** preventable. It takes someone willing to speak up and it also takes a person's willingness to listen.

+ Safety happens by choice and so do incidents. That's why every individual makes a difference.

# EPILOGUE

It had been almost a year since Kurt Bradshaw's promotion to director of global safety, and the past 12 months had raised the bar, not only for Kurt but also for the rest of the company.

His transition, from operations to taking on the challenge of creating a culture of safety, had not been without its glitches. However, the strengths Kurt had developed as a leader over the years were the same skills he required to develop a culture of safety.

With Sam's mentoring, Kurt met management's goal of reversing the skyrocketing number of claims, not to mention the high cost of operational downtime associated with all those injuries and fatalities.

Comparing last quarter's frequency rates to those of the previous year, there was no doubt: The majority of their people around the world had taken ownership of the company's Safety Culture.

The company had no fatalities during the 12-month period. Their Lost Time Incident Rate decreased over 30 percent … and, while there was still an alarming number of Near Hits – something that had not been previously measured – Kurt was pleased to see they were successful in creating an environment where mine workers were now willing to report an incident had even taken place.

The company was leading instead of trailing the industry in terms of safety performance.

The phone rang and Kurt heard Ron Kaiser's voice. "Seen the safety numbers for last quarter?"

"Just going over them now," Kurt replied. "They're continuing to improve – that's the good news."

"I can tell you, the executive management team and board of directors are nothing short of euphoric. The minister of energy even told us our safety record was key to being awarded that large mining permit, and our new safety culture was the hot topic during this quarter's analyst call," Kaiser was almost gushing. "Of course, we're not where we want to be, but as the president said during the safety workshop he attended, 'commitment to building a culture of safety will help us reach our goal of everyone making it safely home to their loved ones.'"

"He's right," Kurt agreed. "Of course, we're never going to eliminate all of the risks, but if we continue to *Make Safety a HABIT*™ by reinforcing the behaviors we want to see through *HABIT*™ *Conversations*, we will set a new standard for the industry."

"Right … right on," Kaiser said, his voice beaming, "Just keep it up. Good job, man!"

Kurt continued to scan the report. As of that quarter, all personnel – more than 10,000 in 20 countries – had completed a behavior-based safety workshop. But Kurt knew there was no 'silver bullet' when it came to training, which is why they were already developing follow-up workshops.

He sat back, proud of what the company had achieved. The return on investment was clearly evident. The reduction in claims cost alone had more than paid for the development and implementation of training. Plus, turnover was down and the company was seeing overall operational improvement resulting in increased tonnage.

"Maybe more importantly, though," Kurt thought to himself, "our miners and our supervisors are actually happier coming to work. They're 'proud to be a part of the team,' as one supervisor commented during a recent workshop."

Another had said, "It's an attitude – this culture of safety – people take their responsibility seriously when it comes to keeping members of the team, as well as themselves, safe. I didn't think I'd ever say this, but safety has become part of everything I do both here and at home. I just see things in an entirely different light."

Just then the phone rang. "Mr. Bradshaw," said the voice at the other end. "Mr. Jacobsen has asked that you come to his office."

"Uh, right away," Kurt responded as he put the receiver in its cradle. Being summoned to the president's office had not happened very often in his career.

As he took the elevator and walked down the hall, Kurt prepared himself. Could it be another crisis in China? Or South America? He was still guessing as he stood in the office doorway.

"Bradshaw – come in, come in." Fred Jacobsen welcomed him warmly, making sure Kurt knew the rest of the people seated in the room.

"Sorry for this spur-of-the-moment meeting, but we've made some decisions, one of which involves your area," Jacobsen continued. "We've all reviewed our safety results and want to tell you how impressed we are. The numbers have never been this good."

Kurt smiled, "Thank you. It's been a team effort."

"Agreed, and we're behind it 100 percent," Jacobsen said. "In fact, the reason we asked you to join us was to let you know we're elevating the importance of safety within the company.

"We recognize truly committing to a culture of safety is integral to the success of our business," the CEO added.

"And," Jacobson continued, "our first step in demonstrating our commitment is to promote you to vice president of health, safety and environment."

Kurt had not expected a promotion … not this soon. "Well," he began, "I'm surprised and flattered, needless to say …."

Just then, Kurt noticed Fred Jacobsen was frowning … and he was looking in Kurt's direction, making the newly announced VP wonder if he had said the wrong thing. Then he saw the reason for Jacobsen's obvious displeasure.

The person seated next to Kurt had leaned his chair back and was balancing on the two back legs.

"Martin …," the president began, "As senior vice president of operations, you've helped the executive team understand the importance of leading by example. However, there is something that concerns me about your safety ...."

Kurt smiled. Clearly, Fred Jacobson believed in the company's new culture of safety ... and he had obviously moved safety from his mind to his heart, where real change takes place.

✦ ✦ ✦ ✦ ✦

Multiple factors provide the framework for, and allow definition of, a behavior-based safety program. What follows are specific attributes of a culture of safety, which enable it to make such a positive and significant difference within a company:

1. Placing emphasis on human behavior provides the understanding required for individuals to incorporate safety into their lives, both on and off the job.

2. Elevating safety from a priority to a core value demonstrates an unwavering commitment in the face of competing objectives, thus enabling the individual to have the courage necessary to address behavior prior to an incident taking place.

3. Identification and elimination of at-risk behaviors addresses the foundation of incidents, while acknowledging risk itself is an inherent part of life.

4. Acknowledging similarities in 'human' culture allows for geographical expansion of a company's culture of safety.

5. Recognition of the interdependency of safety with operations enables a person to utilize leadership skills not unique to safety.

At the risk of sounding redundant, we hope you will use a culture of safety like the one Kurt established in your own personal journey and, as a result, will work to improve safety continuously wherever life takes you.

Remember, real change can only take place where there is an open mind and a willing heart.

# About the Authors

**Gregory M. Anderson** is president and CEO of Randy Smith Training Solutions, a Moody International Company. The company specializes in providing behavior-based safety leadership, teambuilding and intercultural diplomacy for organizations operating in high-risk environments. With offices around the world, the company has conducted workshops for almost 200,000 people in more than 60 countries.

A graduate of the University of Southern California, Greg has lived, worked and traveled in more than 50 countries as he battled oil fires in Kuwait, provided infrastructure for military personnel in Haiti and worked in the energy industry in North Africa.

Greg has been at the forefront of workplace safety and saving lives for more than a decade. He continues working to create incident-free cultures around the globe.

He currently lives in Texas with his wife and three daughters.

**Stephen R. Rosene, SPHR,** is co-founder and principal in Madison River Associates, a consulting firm dedicated to enabling individuals and teams to lead change and transition.

Steve is a third-generation miner with 30 years' experience in the global mining industry. Previously, he led training and development as the director of organizational services for the largest U.S.-owned mining company and was the manager of human resources, safety and security at a major Copper/Moly operation when it received the Sentinels of Safety Award.

Steve has been involved with green-field mining ventures, the startup and rehabilitation of closed mines and the expansion of existing operations in the copper, gold, coal, trona, iron-ore and diamond sectors.

A graduate of the University of Wyoming, Steve has worked with numerous global mining interests. The projects he has been involved with have taken him to most of the major mining regions on four continents.

Steve is a member of the Society for Mining, Metallurgy and Exploration and has served on the SME Coal & Energy Division Scholarship Committee. He also has been an adjunct instructor at Rice University in partnership with the Society for Human Resource Management.

He lives in Texas with his wife and four children.

# ACKNOWLEDGMENTS
## by Greg Anderson

I believe you can learn something from every person you meet. Let me take this opportunity to thank those who have provided me with their knowledge:

Eric Guidry, Robert Suggs, Rick Hicks, Jaime Acero, Ezzat Kamel, Karen Stewart, Jade Strong, and the newest member of our team, Bill Richardson, for the confidence and support they have provided, as well as their hard work, which has enabled us to accomplish so much.

The entire team at Randy Smith Training Solutions – for their hard work and professionalism. You are the finest group of people I have ever had the pleasure of working with.

Brendan Connolly for believing in the value of training, and everyone at Moody International for their uncompromising standards.

Ken Blanchard – who has taught so many of us not only how to become better managers but also how to be better human beings.

Alice Adams – who continues her magic.

Steve Rosene – your knowledge of the mining industry and, more importantly, commitment to the safety of miners allowed us to bring these characters to life. Thank you for sharing your passion so that more people will make it home safely each day.

My parents, Gordon and Elizabeth Anderson – the two finest people on earth. Nothing I could write would express my love and appreciation for all you have given me.

My daughters, Brittany, Makenzie, and Kendall, for always standing up for what you believe in.

Finally, my best friend and wife, who gives so much of herself to others each day.

# ACKNOWLEDGMENTS
## by Stephen R. Rosene

The mining industry and professional miners worldwide have had a profound influence on my life over the past 50+ years. The men and women who have positively impacted me and my family are too numerous to mention. However, my respect for their contributions to their employees, their communities, the minerals industry and, ultimately, to the betterment of our world is profound.

Their passionate commitment to the safety and health of their miners was my inspiration for becoming involved in this book. I have been with them when a miner was lost and when we made the long drive into town to visit the family. I have been with them as they struggled to change at-risk behaviors and guide their miners in making safe choices. This book is dedicated to all of you!

My grandfathers, Walter (Olson) Rosene from Sweden and Sam Goich from Yugoslavia, came to the United States and began our family's mining legacy in the underground coal mines near Rock Springs, Wyoming. My mother, Shirley Goich Rosene, grew up in a coal camp and, from those meager beginnings, she instilled a love for hard work, honesty, tenacity and independence in her children. My father, Carl Rosene, taught me that your reputation was everything and to do your best at all times. To my parents, Carl and Shirley, my brothers, Larry and Kurt and my children, Justin, Cory, Kinsey and Madison, I thank you for your love, your support, your wit and wisdom.

To my wife, Andi, who kept me on course for 25+ years as we journeyed from one mine startup to the next. I love you.

Alice Adams, your patience, tutoring, questioning and writing skills are awesome. Thank you.

Greg Anderson, you provided the opportunity to take my life's passion for improving the safety and health of all workers and put it into a medium that will reach miners around the globe. Thank you. Further, my compliments to you and your professional staff at Randy Smith Training Solutions as you strive to create a zero-incident culture for your clients. Honorable and meaningful work!

# Make Safety a *HABIT*™ in Your Organization

Are you, like Kurt, recognizing the need to reduce incidents and injuries within your organization? Are the costs of claims and lost productivity having a significant impact on the bottom line? Or maybe the organization has a good safety record, but there is concern about keeping the momentum going despite having possibly reached a plateau.

If so, Moody International has the expertise to help you expand your culture of safety and demonstrate the improvement other organizations have achieved. Additional ways we can help *Make Safety a HABIT*™ within your organization include:

## DETERMINING NEEDS

You have limited resources to invest on even the most critical issues; therefore, you want to be sure you're focused on the right ones. Are employees aware of their behavior and the impact it has on safety, or have they grown complacent over time? Are supervisors tolerating at-risk behaviors because of *perceived* pressure? Or is senior management unintentionally sending "mixed messages"? Moody International can help you determine what actions will be most effective in expanding your organization's safety culture.

## SENIOR MANAGEMENT PLANNING

Is senior management uncertain where, how … or if … to start improving your organization's safety performance? Our staff of experienced professionals can design and facilitate an executive team meeting to help clarify the organization's approach to creating a company-wide safety culture and the results that can realistically be accomplished.

## WORKSHOPS

To achieve zero incidents, employees at all levels of the organization need to receive a consistent message about their role in building a strong safety culture and learn skills for turning those responsibilities into action. Moody International curriculum designers and facilitators will work with you to develop and conduct workshops to address your specific objectives while celebrating your organization's many positives.

## ON-SITE COACHING

True behavior change requires ongoing feedback. Moody International can work with your managers on site to develop the skills they need to create a work environment where employees are motivated to want to work safely.

## KEYNOTE ADDRESS

The authors of *Race Against Time*, or another member of their professional team of speakers, can conduct a presentation at your next meeting or conference. Each presentation is customized to address how to **Make Safety a *HABIT*™** within your specific company.

To find out how we can help you **Make Safety a *HABIT*™**, please visit our Web site at www.randysmith.com or call us at 888-682-8182.

# Order Form

1-30 copies  $14.95          31-100 copies  $13.95          100+ copies  $12.95

---

*Race Against Time*                    _____ copies X _____   = $_____

---

Shipping & Handling Charges    $_____

Subtotal                                      $_____

Sales Tax (8% – LA Only)            $_____

**Total (U.S. Dollars Only)        $_____**

## Please Contact Me To Discuss:

❑ Determining Needs                    ❑ On-site Coaching

❑ Senior Management Planning    ❑ Other (please specify) _____

❑ Workshops                                 _____

Contact information:_____

**Domestic U.S. (AK, HI add'l) Shipping & Handling Charges (single point delivery)**

| Total $ Amount | Up to $50 | $51-$99 | $100-$249 | $250-$1199 | $1200-$2999 | $3000+ |
|---|---|---|---|---|---|---|
| Charge | $6 | $9 | $16 | $30 | $80 | $125 |

Name _____ Job Title _____

Organization _____ Phone _____

Shipping Address _____ Fax _____

Billing Address_____ Email _____

City _____ State_____ ZIP_____

❑ Please Invoice (Orders over $500) Purchase Order Number (if applicable)_____

Charge Your Order:              ❑ MasterCard      ❑ Visa     ❑ American Express

Credit Card Number _____ Exp. Date _____

Signature _____

❑ Check Enclosed (Payable to: Randy Smith Training Solutions)

FAX Orders to:  337-235-4494            Mail to:  Randy Smith Training Solutions
Phone:  888-682-8182                                    201 Energy Pkwy., Suite 240
www.RandySmith.com                                        Lafayette, LA 70508